# What a disgusting display!

Not two hours after he'd been trying to sweet-talk *her* into an affair, he'd come on to a girl half his age. Well, maybe not half, but *years* younger. And he was the one who had been so worried about her being hung up on an older man!

I'm jealous, Anne thought. And she'd actually been on the verge of falling in love with the rat! Thank heaven she'd come to her senses in time.

**Dear Reader**

For many of us, this is the best period of the year—the season of goodwill and celebration—though it can make big demands on your time and pocket, too! Or maybe you prefer to spend these mid-winter months more quietly? Whatever you've got planned, Mills & Boon's romances are always there for you as special friends at the turn of the year: easy, entertaining and comforting reads that are great value for money. Stay warm, won't you!

*The Editor*

**Rosemary Hammond** grew up in California, but has since lived in several other states. Rosemary and her husband have travelled extensively throughout the United States, Mexico, the Caribbean and Canada, both with and without their two sons. She enjoys gardening, music and needlework, but her greatest pleasure has always been reading. She started writing romances because she enjoyed them, but also because the mechanics of fiction fascinated her and she thought they might be something she could do.

**Recent titles by the same author:**

THE HOUSE ON CHARTRES STREET

# ISLAND OF LOVE

BY

## ROSEMARY HAMMOND

MILLS & BOON LIMITED
ETON HOUSE   18-24 PARADISE ROAD
RICHMOND   SURREY   TW9 1SR

*First published in Great Britain 1992
by Mills & Boon Limited*

© Rosemary Hammond 1992

*Australian copyright 1992
Philippine copyright 1993
This edition 1993*

ISBN 0 263 77859 2

*Set in Times Roman 10½ on 12 pt.
01-9301-51383 C*

*Made and printed in Great Britain*

# CHAPTER ONE

THE telephone call came on a Thursday night in early November. Anne was curled up in an easychair in the living-room of her apartment, listening to the eternal rain slashing against the window and struggling half-heartedly with the special feature article on Christmas in the north-west that Jerry had assigned to her.

She'd broken her rule and was drinking an after-dinner cup of coffee, Starbuck's French mocha, enjoying every wicked sip, Sinatra singing softly in the background, one of those three-hour fire logs flickering feebly in the small brick fireplace.

She picked up the telephone at the first ring, glad of the interruption. 'Hello.'

'Anne?' It was a man's voice, vaguely familiar. 'Anne Cameron?'

'Yes.'

'This is Arnold Pembroke. You may not remember me.'

She had to think a minute, but in just a few seconds she was able to picture him in her mind. 'Mr Pembroke! Of course I remember you.' She laughed nervously and ran a hand over her short dark hair. 'It's just been so long that I couldn't quite place you at first.'

'Yes, it has been a long time,' he replied. 'Must be over ten years by now, in fact. How have you been, Anne?'

'Oh, quite well. Working hard.'

There was a small silence. Scenes from the past seemed to flash before Anne's very eyes from the moment she'd heard him speak his name and she'd been able to put a face to the voice. More than a face, a personality, a person who'd been an intimate part of her girlhood, her father's good friend. So many questions rose up in her mind that she hardly knew where to start. The most important one at the moment, however, was why he was calling her at all after so many years of silence.

'Are you here in Seattle?' she asked finally.

'No, I'm calling from my office at Friday Harbor. Working late, as usual. Trying to catch up.' He cleared his throat. 'Anne, I'm afraid I have some bad news for you. Your father died suddenly last week. It was quite unexpected. I'm sorry.'

Anne sank back against the cushions, closed her eyes and tried to picture her father. The last time she'd seen him he'd been so angry at her that he could hardly speak, except to shout at her to get out of his house, out of his sight, that he never wanted to set eyes on her again.

'I see,' she said at last in a small voice.

'I've been trying to get in touch with you,' the lawyer went on briskly. 'You know, for the funeral. We—er—buried him on Monday.'

'I'm sorry. I've been out of town for the past week on a story for my magazine and just got back this afternoon.' She cleared her throat. 'How did he die?'

'Coronary. It was quick anyway. Not a bad way to go.'

'No.'

There was another silence. He seemed to be waiting for her to say something, burst into tears, express some kind of emotion, at least ask for details, but all she felt was a creeping numbness. Like a door suddenly slamming, the final chapter of her youth was now closed, over and done with.

He began speaking again, in the same brisk tone of voice. 'I don't know if you were aware that I've been handling his legal affairs for some time. He named you as sole beneficiary in his will. There's not a lot of money, just a few thousand, but there is the property, the house, and a small insurance policy.'

Anne sat bolt upright. 'You mean he left everything to me? I can't believe it. There must be some mistake. It's been years since we had any contact at all.'

'There's no mistake,' was the dry, toneless reply. 'I drew up the will myself.'

'When?'

'I don't know offhand. A few years ago. It's watertight. No question of another will, and I can attest that he was of sound mind when he executed this one.'

'I'm sorry, Mr Pembroke. I didn't mean to doubt your word. It's just such a shock. I had no idea he'd leave me a bean, much less everything. Even the farm.'

'Who else would he leave it to? And, as I said, there's not much of an estate. I'm named as executor, but as his beneficiary there are certain things only you can decide.'

'I see,' she said slowly. 'What do you want me to do?'

'That depends. I can take care of everything up here if you like, then mail you a cheque when the probate closes, but I do have to know what you want to do about the house and property.'

'Do? What is there to do?'

'Well, do you intend to keep it or sell it?'

'I don't really know. Probably sell it. I suppose something will have to be done about the animals.'

'There are no animals. He sold off all the sheep last year.'

'I see.'

'Well, at any rate, if you're sure you want to sell the place, I can handle all the legal details, but I think you'd better come on up here and go through his things.'

'Why?' she said, panicking. 'Why do I have to do that?'

'It all belongs to you now, Anne. You have to make the decisions regarding the disposition of furniture, his personal belongings, that kind of thing.'

'Can't you do that? I'm sorry, Mr Pembroke, I don't mean to be difficult, but I just don't think I could face coming back to the island again——' Her voice broke off.

'I understand,' came the quick reply. 'I can do it if you really want me to.'

'Oh, please.'

'All right, then, we'll leave it at that. I'll go on up there one day next week and see to things myself.'

'Thank you,' she said. 'I'd really appreciate that.'

After they hung up, Anne sat there for a long time staring blankly into the fire until the last embers slowly flickered out. As the stark reality of her father's death took hold in her mind, the fact that he was gone now for good, a wave of terrible regret swept over her.

It was too late now to make it up with him. She should have tried long ago. She could picture him now as he'd been when she was a child—a rather remote man, preoccupied with his farm, his sheep, but a man

of high principle, a fair man, a good husband, a loving
father in his way. Until that last awful night...

It was then that the tears began to fall, and she
buried her face in her hands, sobbing.

Later, lying wakeful in her bed, she went over and
over the conversation with Arnold Pembroke. It had
cost her so much through the years to keep every
painful memory of her father at bay that her first in-
stinctive reaction had been self-protective. She wanted
no part of his estate, not the money, not the house,
no mementoes of her girlhood, nothing from the past
at all.

Now, however, she was being hurtled back into that
past whether she liked it or not. The news of her
father's death, and especially the fact that he'd left
everything to her, had touched her more than she
would ever have thought possible. The way she'd left
the island after the terrible row with him—sneaking
off in the night with no farewells, not even a note to
the people she cared about the most, especially people
like Ben and Victoria Poole—still had the power to
shame her.

Mr Pembroke had said he'd take care of all the
practical details, selling the house, disposing of her
father's personal belongings, winding up his business
affairs. All she'd have to do was sit down here in
Seattle, getting on with her own life, and in the end
he'd send her a cheque.

But was the life she planned to get on with all that
great? Something had been missing from it for so long
that she'd almost become accustomed to the emp-
tiness, the pointlessness of it all, filling her days with
frantic work on the magazine, agreeing to every one
of Jerry's unreasonable requests, making jokes about

her slave-driving boss, but in truth grateful for the distraction.

Tonight's telephone call emphasised just how aimless her existence really was compared with the life she'd left behind ten years ago, the person she'd been then. A good part of herself was contained in that village, that house. Memories of her dead mother rose up in her mind, and of David, the adored older brother. How could she just let someone else dispose of what might remain of them?

It came to her then that she had to go herself, that no matter how her father had felt about her she owed it to him to do this one last thing for him. Jerry wouldn't like it, but she'd just have to risk his wrath. She'd catered to his whims and totally unreasonable demands for so long that surely he owed her this one favour.

'Two weeks!' Jerry shook his dark head vigorously. 'Out of the question.'

The interview was turning out pretty much as Anne had expected it would, negative to the point of flat refusal. She'd gone straight to his office first thing that Friday morning, hadn't even stopped to hang up her coat or set her bag down on her desk, not only because Jerry was one of those people who was always at his best in the early hours, but for fear she would lose her nerve and change her mind again if she delayed the confrontation.

Although it was fifteen minutes before the official start of the working day, he was already there, as she knew he would be, sitting behind his cluttered desk, bent over the layout for the December issue of the magazine, his head in his hands, groaning softly to himself.

'Jerry, have you got a minute?'

He looked up at her, sheer agony etched in every feature. 'What is it?' he barked. He picked up the glossy sheets on his desk and waved them at her. 'If I've told that blankety-blank fashion editor once, I've told her a dozen times——'

'Jerry,' she broke in. 'I just received word last night that my father died.'

He stared blankly at her for a moment, as if she'd just brought him a message from Mars. 'Oh,' he said at last, obviously doing his best to look sympathetic, but not succeeding very well. 'Sorry.'

'I'm afraid I'll need some time off—you know, to go on up to Mystic Harbor, take care of things.'

He eyed her suspiciously. 'How much time?'

She shrugged. 'Well, I thought two weeks.'

It was then he exploded, just as she'd anticipated. He leapt up from his chair and began pacing around the office in his typical long-legged stride. As she watched him, listening to the sound of the rain slashing against the window, the traffic noises drifting up from Union Street, twenty storeys below, she was torn between asserting herself to pry out of him the leave that was hers by rights anyway, and cowardly relief at the thought that if he flatly refused she wouldn't have to go.

Still, she had to try. 'Jerry, my father just died. There are things I have to do.'

He came to stand before her, braced his lean hips back against the desk and glared down at her. 'How long have you been working on the magazine, Anne?'

She gave him a startled look. 'A little over five years. Why?'

'In all that time I never once heard you mention that you even had a father, much less that you cared anything about him. Now why, all of a sudden, is it so important for you to dash up to that dinky island of yours for two weeks to settle his affairs? Can't his lawyer take care of that?'

'He could, but it's really my responsibility. Come on, Jerry, I can work on the Christmas feature article just as well up there as I can here in Seattle. Call it compassionate leave—which I am entitled to, according to the terms of my contract, if you recall.'

He gave her a humourless smile. 'You should know by now, Anne, that I'm not a compassionate man.' He straightened up and stared out of the window, chin in hand, thinking it over. 'All right,' he said grudgingly at last. 'But two weeks is too long. Today is Friday. You can go up this afternoon, get your business taken care of over the weekend, and be back on Monday.'

She squared her shoulders and lifted her chin at him. 'No,' she said firmly. 'I need more time than that. A week at least.'

He threw up his hands. 'All right, you win. A week.'

'Thank you,' she said stiffly, and turned to go.

It wasn't until she reached the door that it dawned on her that she'd been out-manoeuvred again. She'd been determined to squeeze the whole two weeks out of him, and somehow had ended up getting only one. He'd even managed to make that seem like a major concession.

She wasn't going to let him get away with it this time. Except for the week she'd been down with a strep throat two winters ago, she hadn't been out sick a day in over five years, not to mention that she'd worked most holidays. He'd even managed to cut every vacation short by calling her at home and sending her out on assignments he claimed only she could handle.

She turned around, her mouth open, ready to do battle, to see him walking slowly towards her, rubbing his chin thoughtfully. 'Say,' he said. 'Doesn't that famous artist live on your island? What's his name? Ben Poole?'

Anne stared at him. 'Yes, he does. What about it?'

'Do you know him?'

'I used to.'

'OK, you can have your two weeks.' He held up a hand. 'Provided you get an interview with Poole and bring back a feature article. With photographs.'

Anne sighed. 'Jerry, he doesn't give interviews. You know that.'

Jerry grinned. 'But he might, as a favour to a personal friend.'

She shook her head. 'I don't think so. He's a very private man. Besides, I haven't even seen him in years.'

Jerry put a hand on her arm, leaned towards her and adopted his most confidential tone. 'Listen, Anne, you're my best interviewer. Didn't you get in to see Nancy Reagan when she was in town and no one else could get near her? And that great piece you did on Mel Gibson when he was filming here?'

He was getting excited now, warming to the project. Nothing could stem the tide once he'd seized hold of a pet idea. In that mood he was like a dog guarding a particularly delectable bone. It was even rather amusing to watch the dramatic metamorphosis in his attitude once he glimpsed the possibility of benefit to himself, the expression on his sharp, intelligent face moving from blank-eyed resistance to dawning self-interest.

Anne knew it was hopeless to argue. Still, she had to try. The mere prospect of seeing Ben again after what happened last time, much less ask him for an interview, was too awful even to contemplate.

'Listen, Jerry. I know him. He lives like a perfect recluse. All that ever mattered to him was his painting, probably even more so since his wife died last year. They were very close.'

Jerry nodded vigorously. 'Good. That's a great angle.'

She shook her head. 'I'm sorry, Jerry, I just can't do it, intrude on his privacy like that. I *won't* do it.'

Jerry's mouth flew open, clearly shocked at the un-expected firmness of her tone. He wasn't used to such insubordination and seemed to be genuinely bewil-dered by it, at a loss how to handle it. However, he hadn't become the owner of a growing string of magazines for nothing. Recovering swiftly, he folded his arms across his chest and fixed her with a gimlet eye.

'Now you listen to me, Cameron,' he said in the deceptively gentle tones that always meant a storm was brewing. 'Ben Poole is one of the north-west's greatest natural resources, a painter whose work is recognised all over the world. Even an artistic moron like me knows that. And no one can get near him.' He shook his head slowly from side to side with an expression of ineffable sorrow. 'Now, are you seriously going to tell me you won't even try?'

That was her plan exactly, and she opened her mouth to tell him so, but before she could get a word out he'd raised a hand to stop her.

'Sit down, Anne,' he said in a deceptively calm tone. He motioned her to the chair in front of his desk.

She slowly sank on to it and gazed up at him warily, wondering what diabolical scheme had popped into his head this time. He was leaning back against the desk, his arms folded across his chest, giving her such a long appraising look that it took all her will-power to keep from flinching from those steady deep brown eyes.

'There's more going on here than you're telling me,' he said at last. 'Just what is this guy Poole to you? Personally, I mean.'

Anne could feel the warm flush spreading over her face. She squirmed uncomfortably in her chair and looked away. She couldn't help it. Not only was she flustered by his uncanny ability to put his finger on her sorest spot, but for the first time in living memory he was looking at her as if she was a real human being instead of merely a cog in his well-oiled machine.

'N-nothing,' she faltered. 'When I knew Ben he was not only married to my best friend, but he was so crazy in love with her, no other woman even existed for him.'

Jerry raised one heavy dark eyebrow, a habit Anne had come to deeply mistrust, and pursed his lips in a dubious expression of disbelief. '"The lady doth protest too much, methinks,"' he quoted softly. 'Come on, Anne, what's going on here?'

Anne didn't know what to do. If she tried to speak, she knew she'd only end up sputtering, but she had to say something, anything to wipe that unnerving, smug, knowing look off his face. She opened her mouth, hoping something would come to her, but just then the telephone on his desk jangled.

As he turned from her to snatch it up, annoyance etched in every feature, she slumped back in her chair, grateful for the reprieve.

'Yes!' he snarled into the telephone. He listened for a moment, still frowning. 'Oh, hell, I guess you'd better put her on.'

There was a short pause. Anne watched in growing amusement as he tried to reassemble his features into something besides the annoyance he obviously felt at the interruption. It wasn't a success, however, since his dark eyes remained narrowed, the firm jaw hard. One long leg was swinging back and forth—a typical gesture from a man with more pent-up energy than Anne had ever encountered in another human being.

From his reaction, she knew the caller had to be one of the tall svelte blondes he was notorious for squiring around town. If office gossip could be believed, Jerry's amorous adventures were as intense as they were short, and, from the signs, he was getting ready to bid farewell to yet another one. Anne got up to go, but he waved her back down in the chair, a sure sign that the conversation was going to be short.

'Oh, hello, Claudia,' he said at last into the telephone.

As he listened to the clearly audible squawk coming from the other end of the line, the frown deepened and the leg began to swing back and forth more rapidly. Anne was a little embarrassed at having to witness his discomfiture, but relieved that at least it got her off the hook so that she could recover her own composure. It was also rather entertaining to see him in action.

'Listen,' he said, at last, obviously cutting Claudia short. 'I'm tied up right now. I'll call you back.'

Without waiting for a reply, he broke the connection. He stood there for a few moments, slightly turned away from Anne, his hand still on the receiver, his gaze fixed on some point out of the window. He was rubbing his chin pensively, as though plotting his next move, and Anne had to feel a little sorry for poor Claudia, who was clearly about to get dumped. In Anne's view no man was worth the kind of treatment Jerry dished out to his blondes, who still seemed to pursue him relentlessly.

However, watching him now, she had to admit that he was an attractive man, if you liked the aggressive dynamo type. There was a kind of restless coiled energy in him that made it seem as if he was always in motion, even when he was sitting still. He couldn't be called handsome—his features were too strong for that, and his thick unruly shock of dark mahogany-coloured hair always seemed to need cutting. His best feature was his eyes, a really beautiful deep liquid shade of brown, and he was well-built, in a lithe, sinewy kind of way.

Just then he crossed over to her side of the desk and perched on the edge of it, his arms folded in front of him, a challenging look in his eyes.

'Well,' he said.

She eyed him warily. 'Well, what?'

He pointed a finger at her. 'What's that knowing smile all about?'

She sobered instantly. 'I'm sorry. I didn't mean to smile.'

'You've got something on your mind, haven't you?'
He tossed his head towards the telephone. 'About
that.'

She gave him her most innocent look. 'Well, you're
wrong. It's none of my business what you get up to
with your blondes, although I must say——'

'See?' he crowed gleefully, waving a hand in the
air. 'I knew it.' He leaned over until his face was only
inches away from hers. 'What's the matter, Anne?
Don't you approve of me?'

She narrowed her eyes and opened her mouth, ready
to object more strenuously, but instead found herself
gazing into those deep brown depths, held there by
some invisible force. She could see the tiny lines at
the corners of his eyes, the way his thick dark lashes
swept the high cheekbones, and was suddenly
speechless.

His expression was dead serious, his eyes slightly
widened, as though he was as much at a loss as she.
Then he cocked his head to one side, smiled quirkily
and gave her a cool, appraising look.

'Little Miss Touch-Me-Not,' he murmured, leaning
closer. 'Actually, I think I'm getting a little tired of
blondes.'

While she stared up at him blankly, unable to move,
he raised a hand, as though to touch her. But he drew
it back quickly, just as though it had been burned.
He jumped to his feet and began pacing around the
room.

'All right, where were we?'

Still dazed, Anne stared at him for a moment, then
gave herself a little shake. 'I was just explaining to
you why I couldn't get that interview you wanted with
Ben Poole,' she said slowly.

A familiar sly grin curled on his thin mouth. 'There'll be a fat bonus in it for you if you pull it off.'

Anne eyed him carefully. 'How much?'

He shrugged. 'Let's say in the neighbourhood of a thousand dollars.'

Anne shook her head. 'No, Jerry. I've had too much sad experience with your famous "neighbourhoods". I want a firm commitment—in writing—for one thousand dollars, to be paid on delivery of the article.'

He threw up his hands. 'Lord, you're getting to be a hard case, Anne. What happened to the sweet co-operative girl I hired?'

'I don't know, Jerry. You tell me. Sheer instinct for survival maybe?'

'All right. You draw up the agreement and I'll sign it. But for God's sake don't tell anyone.'

He glanced over at the glass partition that separated his room from the rapidly filling outer office, then slid off the desk and went over to the door and closed it. He came striding back to her, grabbed her by the arm and pulled her up out of her chair.

'Now, here's the way we'll work it,' he said in a low voice. 'You can go on up there today——'

'No,' she broke in firmly. 'Not today. The ferry traffic is impossible on Friday afternoon. Besides, I need the weekend to make arrangements.'

'What arrangements?' he asked in honest amazement. According to Jerry, all one had to do to prepare for any trip was walk out of the door, get in the car and go.

She held up a hand and began to tick off on her fingers. 'I need to get my clothes ready, pack, stop the paper, arrange for one of the neighbours to pick up my mail. I have to call my father's lawyer, to let him know I'm coming...'

He threw up his hands. 'All right. Tomorrow, then.'

'Monday.'

Their eyes locked together in mortal combat. He hated to give in—it was against all his most cherished principles of management—but Anne asserted herself like this so rarely that when she did he had to know she really meant it. He'd conned her into doing the job, and she wasn't going to budge on how she went about it. Once she let Jerry take control of the project, she'd be lost.

He waved a hand in the air. ''Whatever. In any case, as soon as you get the interview set up, give me a call and I'll send up a photographer. You can have anyone you want.' He gave her a smug look that was meant to be magnanimous.

'That won't work, Jerry. Look, it's just barely possible that for old times' sake, as a personal favour to me, Ben might agree to an interview. But he'd never stand for a photographer. What's more, I wouldn't even ask. Jerry, the man is paranoid about his privacy. Can't you understand that?'

'OK, then you take a camera up there yourself. You know how to use it, I hope?'

'Yes, of course. I'll take it, but I won't guarantee I'll get any pictures.'

'I have every confidence, Anne, that you'll do your very best to earn that thousand dollars,' As usual, he was bent on getting in the last word.

Over the weekend, as Anne made preparations for her trip, tasks not nearly so onerous or time-consuming as she'd made out to Jerry, she already regretted the stubborn determination that had made her insist on extracting the leave out of him in the first place, much less agree to the interview with Ben. If she'd only let well enough alone, bowed as usual to his refusal to let her go for longer than a weekend, she would have had the perfect excuse.

Now she was committed. She would have to face Ben again. Had he changed? Would he remember that awful night she'd blurted out her love for him? Thrown herself at him? Even now, ten years later, the memory of that scene had the power to fill her with hot shame.

Every time she thought about the ordeal that lay ahead of her, the incipient dread at the prospect blossomed into full flower, her stomach would start to churn and she would curse the impulse that had tricked her into changing her mind.

Early Monday morning Anne set off on the drive north from Seattle to Anacortes on the busy interstate in a vicious sleety rain that pounded on the front windscreen so that she could scarcely see the road and had to creep along so slowly that she'd almost missed the ferry at Anacortes.

And it wasn't over yet. After she stopped at Arnold Pembroke's office in Friday Harbor, she still had another drive ahead of her up to Roche Harbor at the northern tip of the island, where she would leave her car. She'd arranged to meet Patrick Fielding there to take her across the narrow channel to Mystic Harbor on his fishing boat. In the heavy seas, she wasn't looking forward to it, but it was the only means of transport to the village except for seaplane.

The ferry groaned its way out of the harbour, its bulk bumping against the wooden pilings, and through a steady chop began to wind its way around the smaller islands on its regular run to Friday Harbor, the metropolis of the chain, situated at the southern tip of San Juan Island and protected by a small sheltered bay.

Once safely aboard, her car parked on the vehicle deck, the engine switched off, Anne climbed the inside staircase up to the upper deck and made her way to the stern. She stood there, her arms braced on the railing, the strong breeze tearing at her scarf, leaning over and staring fixedly down at the deep blue of the sea. No other body of water she had ever seen was coloured that particular shade—a darkish, clear, somehow mysterious hue that seemed to be more an amalgam of every possible variation of blue than a distinct colour.

As she gazed, mesmerised, into its depths, she was seized by a sudden strange emotional state, as though she had stepped from one plane of existence to another in the blink of an eye, like entering a room expecting to see familiar objects, and finding instead that the furnishings, carpet, wall coverings—even colours— were strange, alien, perhaps dimly recalled from the distant past, even another life.

The foaming wake, the screech of the gulls as they wheeled and dipped overhead, the salty tang of the chill air, the powerful rolling waves beneath the surface as they made their inexorable way to and from the shore, crashing against the huge boulders that surrounded the island, filled her with a familiar shuddering thrill.

From earliest childhood the sea had evoked in Anne both an odd feeling of melancholy and an exhilarating, heart-piercing joy, curiously joined into a transcendent state whose power over her was irresistible. Now, after her long absence, there was superimposed upon it a feeling of nostalgia for what might have been, what never was, so strong that it rapidly grew into an actual physical pain.

Then the first few drops of rain began to fall, pattering softly on her face and hair, settling on her mouth and eyelashes, and the moment passed. She looked up towards the horizon. Friday Harbor was dead ahead. She turned and went down to the lower deck and reached her car just as the blast of the ferry announced its arrival and the chains began to clank.

After stopping at Arnold Pembroke's office in Friday Harbor to pick up the keys to the house from his secretary, she drove north to Roche Harbor, where Patrick was waiting for her. They made the harrowing trip across the channel on his boat in a nasty squall, the waves washing over the decks in great torrents.

As they turned into the sheltered inlet that led to the harbour, and Anne had her first glimpse of the village dead ahead, her heart started to pound so hard that her whole body shook. It was as though she had been dead and was now being brought alive again, panting and groaning, by an irresistible force.

Apparently nothing at all had changed since the day she left. There was the little white church in the foreground, high atop the hill, the low storm-weathered shops and small fishermen's cottages behind it, the one hotel. At least the rain had stopped, and a pale wintry sun was struggling to break through the remaining clouds.

She helped Patrick tie up his boat at the landing, and when it was secure he offered to drive her home, but she declined, partly because she knew he still had

things on the boat to tend to after the choppy ride,
but mostly because she wanted to arrive at the house
alone. She didn't need a witness to whatever emotion
the sight of her old home, long abandoned, would
arouse in her.

After thanking Patrick, she walked up from the
dock to the tiny village, deserted now in the off-
season, slinking through the one paved street like a
criminal, hoping no one would see her. She still had
half a mile to go, and by the time she reached the
unpaved road that wound along the ridge high above
Smugglers Cove the early November dusk was beginning to fall.

She plodded on, going further inland now as the
road turned away from the sea, lugging her one
suitcase every step of the way, and it was dark when
she reached her father's house.

My house now, she thought, and stepped inside.

# CHAPTER TWO

THE minute Anne crossed the threshold she was struck by a dismal sense of decay in the damp, musty air, even in the very shapes of the familiar furniture against the stark white walls, shadowed now in the gathering dusk. She stood rigid in the doorway for a full minute, like an animal who instinctively sensed danger in a lair long abandoned.

Perhaps it was only the southerly wind gusting up from the Straits of Juan de Fuca, carrying before it the heavy black rain clouds so typical in these northern islands in the autumn, rain that was spattering now against the windows. Or the long, tiring trip. Or, most likely, her own precarious state of nerves at the prospect of having to face all the spectres from the past which she had so foolishly imagined were long buried.

She shook herself and took a step inside, closing the door behind her. She fumbled for the light-switch in the entry hall, relieved to see that the power had been left on, and gazed around the old familiar room. There was her mother's rocking-chair by the window, her father's worn leather easychair in front of the stone fireplace, the old roll-top desk by the window where he'd kept his careful livestock records.

It was pitch-dark outside by now. Through the thin curtains at the window she could see the ghostly shapes of the leafless birch trees swaying black in the wind against the night sky. Shuddering, she ran over to pull down the shade against the depressing sight.

Suddenly from behind her there arose a sudden loud jangling sound that reverberated eerily in the empty house. Shocked to the core, she clutched at her throat and gazed wildly around. Her head started spinning so crazily that she was actually afraid she'd fall in a dead faint any minute. She squeezed her eyes shut and covered her ears with her hands, but still the sound kept coming.

Then it finally dawned on her that the awful noise was only the telephone, still ringing insistently. Shamefaced at her cowardly panic, she opened her eyes, and ran to answer it.

'Hello,' she said breathlessly.

'Well?' came a familiar deep baritone voice.

She sank down on the chair beside the telephone. 'Oh, it's you,' she said. Although she felt oddly comforted by the sound of his voice, she knew it wouldn't do to let him know that. 'What do you want, Jerry?'

'What do I want?' he asked in exaggerated surprise. 'I want to know how you're coming along with the interview. You must realise by now that I'm not so free with my two-week leaves that I'm just going to ignore you. I intend to check on your progress often.'

'Jerry, I just now walked inside the door,' she said with a sigh. 'Why are you calling me now? You knew I wasn't even planning to come up here until today.'

'Oh. Well. I guess I forgot.'

She ground her back teeth together in sheer frustration. This from a man who had never, since she'd known him, forgotten the slightest detail of anything remotely connected to his precious magazine. Then it dawned on her that there had been a distinctly sheepish quality to his voice that was totally out of character, and her eyes widened in amazement. Could it possibly be that his concern was actually for her personal welfare?

'Jerry,' she said carefully, 'I'm a big girl. I can take care of myself. This is not exactly the ends of the earth, you know.'

'What's that got to do with anything?' he demanded sternly.

She had to laugh. 'You were worried about me, weren't you? Come on, admit it.'

'The only thing I'm worried about is my story,' he said in a stiff voice.

'Well, I'll tell you what. If you'll admit you were worried about me, I'll admit I was feeling a little shaky right before you called—you know, coming all alone into an empty house this way at night—and was actually glad to hear the sound of your voice. How about it? Is it a deal?'

He gave a hoarse bark of a laugh. 'Not on your life, lady. You said it yourself. You're a big girl. You can take care of yourself. Why should I worry about you?'

'No reason in the world,' she retorted drily. 'I just lost my head there for a minute.'

'Well, that's all right, then. Just don't forget why you're up in that God-forsaken place and why I let you talk me into letting you go for such an unconscionable length of time.'

She bit back a sharp report. 'I won't,' she said sweetly.

'All right, then, I'll check with you later in the week.'

Before she could say anything the telephone clicked loudly in her ear. As she replaced the receiver, she had to smile to herself. In spite of his denial, she knew quite well he'd only called to check on her personally, not the story at all, and it touched her to see this unexpected caring side to him, an aspect of his character he normally kept very well concealed.

Suddenly the brief scene in the office with him on Friday after his telephone conversation with Claudia popped into her mind. She'd been too busy with her preparations for the trip ever since to have given it much thought, but now, after talking to him, she recalled quite vividly just how he had looked at her, and how that look had made her feel.

The furthest thing from her mind during the years she had worked for him was any thought of attraction between them. She knew she wasn't his type. The long string of blondes that trooped in and out of his life during those years was clear evidence of that. He'd never come remotely near making a pass at her, or even looked at her as though she was a desirable woman.

Until Friday. Was it because she had mildly asserted herself for the first time in living memory? Had there really been a glimmer of interest in her as a woman in those dark eyes, or was it only her imagination? More to the point, was *she* attracted to *him*?

At the mere idea of that unlikely event, she laughed aloud in the silence of the empty room. Might as well put her neck in a hangman's noose as get too near *that* devouring flame. Talk about playing with fire!

In any event, she felt much better after talking to him, not nearly so desolate as she had before he called, and she suddenly realised she was ravenously hungry. She'd eaten practically nothing all day, only the sketchy breakfast she'd choked down in her apartment that morning. Later she'd drunk half of a really awful cup of coffee on the ferry, and its dregs were still churning bitterly in her empty stomach.

She went into the kitchen and rummaged in the cupboards for a while, but all she could find were some stale crackers and a jar of peanut butter. Deciding she wasn't *that* hungry, she retrieved her suitcase and handbag and carried them down the narrow hallway to her old bedroom.

She was curious to see what her father had done with it after she left. Boarded it up, most likely, anxious to obliterate every trace of her. Her footsteps creaked on the worn floorboards, as though no one had walked that way for years.

Inside, the curtains were drawn shut, the room pitch-dark. She switched on the bleak overhead light and scanned the room, once again filled with a vague feeling of apprehension. Her eyes darted over the familiar objects—her old dresser, the little pink flowered slipper chair by the window, the braided rug her mother had made, the narrow bed, which, she saw to her surprise, was made up.

Undressing quickly, she put on her nightgown, turned off the light, and slid in between the icy sheets.

There was frost on the ground the next morning, with a bright sun shining in a deep blue sky. Anne was awakened by the soft guttural 'twee-twee' of the mountain chickadees, punctuated by the piercing squawk of a Stellar's jay high in the branches of the towering firs that surrounded her father's property. *Her* property now. She'd slept heavily, dreamlessly, and her brief sense of disorientation at finding herself in a strange bed vanished the moment she got her first tangy whiff of salt water and tideflats.

She opened her eyes to a room filled with sunshine. Tossing the covers aside, she slipped out of bed and went over to the window. The eerie shapes and for-bidding darkness had been replaced with the bright clear landscape so familiar to her from her childhood.

Down below was the pasture where the sheep had grazed, and beyond the meadow stretched the ever-present slate-blue water of the islands. Further westward, past the Haro Straits, rose the huge land mass of Vancouver Island. To the south, beyond the Strait of Juan de Fuca, towered the majestic snow-capped Olympic mountain range on the Washington mainland.

The smaller islands stretched out as far as the eye could see, like emeralds set in a sapphire sea, an in-comparable sight, surely one of the most beautiful in the world, and for the first time since she'd arrived Anne began to feel at home.

She was also freezing. The bare wooden floor was cold on her feet, and she shivered in her thin nightgown. The whole house was like ice and the cold seemed to penetrate to her very bones.

After a quick wash, she dressed hurriedly in black woollen trousers and heavy white turtleneck sweater. As she brushed her short dark hair in front of the mirror over the dresser, her eye was caught by an old snapshot stuck in the bottom corner, cracked and fading, the edges torn. In the picture were three people—Anne herself in the middle, and on either side of her, towering over her, Ben and Victoria Poole. She prised it away from the glass, and as she examined it the exact details of that day were as clear to her as though it had been yesterday.

They were standing in the sunshine on the rocks below the high cliff of Smugglers Cove, the surf pounding in the background. Her mother had taken the picture. In fact, it must have been the summer she died, since Anne looked to be around eighteen. Ben was grinning into the camera, his thick wiry mane of golden hair blowing in the breeze, and Victoria, not much shorter than her husband, was smiling up at him.

As she gazed down at the old photograph, all the old overpowering adolescent feelings rose up in her again, sweeping over her in great waves. Ben had been her ideal of what a man should be—father, brother, friend, husband, lover. Everything had changed now, and she had a sudden strong urge to see him again.

It was still quite early, only a little after nine o'clock. Even though her empty stomach was growling ominously, Anne still couldn't face those stale crackers, so she slipped into her red down-filled parka and set off for the village to pick up some groceries.

Halfway there she came to a crossroads. To the left, down a steep cliff, was Smugglers Cove. To the right, about half a mile distant through a thick wooded copse, was the Poole house. She stood there for a moment, debating, tempted to turn on to that second path. But it was too soon. Better to let their first meeting happen naturally.

It was the off-season in the village, free from the tourists who descended on it between the end of May

and the first of September, and only a few shops
stayed open. In the centre of the one main street sat
the Mystic Harbor Hotel, run by the Sorensons, and
kept open marginally for the natives all year round.

It had used to be the local meeting place for the
villagers during the long winter evenings when even
the hardiest fishermen visiting the island were rare.
Whole families would gather in the large dining-
room—local fishermen whose living depended on their
catch, sheep ranchers like her father, shop owners, a
few retired people—to play cards, listen to the amateur
musicians, even dance a little, the men on one side of
the room drinking, the women on the other knitting
and gossiping.

As Anne went up the weathered wooden steps that
led to the wide front porch, she wondered if the
Sorensons even ran the hotel any more. She stepped
inside and glanced around the empty foyer. Nothing
had changed.

She started down the narrow corridor that led to
the dining-room, which also looked exactly as she remembered it, ten square wooden tables covered in red
checked cloths, the small raised platform at the far
end where the local musicians played, the tall narrow
windows overlooking the sea with the same faded
patterned draperies hanging limply on either side of
them.

She stepped through the swinging door into the
warm kitchen to be greeted by the delicious aroma of
fresh baking in the air. Carl Sorenson was there
bending over the sink, scouring out a muffin tin. At
the sound of Anne's footsteps, he turned around
slowly and stared at her blankly for a moment. Then

the light of recognition dawned in his pale blue eyes, and he gave her a smile of genuine welcome.

'If it isn't Anne Cameron!' he said. 'You've come home.'

'Yes, I've come home,' she said with a smile. 'Temporarily, at least. It's nice to see you again, Carl.'

'You're looking fine, Anne,' he said, wiping his hands on his apron. 'Pretty as a picture and all grown up.' He held out a hand.

'Why, thank you, Carl.' She grasped his hand and shook it warmly. 'I was wondering if I could get some breakfast before I do my grocery shopping. There's nothing at the house fit to eat.'

'Sure thing, Anne. What would you like? Bacon and eggs all right? There are fresh blueberry muffins.'

She sat down at the table in the centre of the room. 'That sounds great. What I'd really like right now is a good cup of coffee. You always did make the best, better than anything I've had in Seattle.'

He flushed, pleased, and poured her a cup from the steaming pot on the stove. While she drank it, he set a place for her at the table, then went back to the stove to start her breakfast. As he fried the bacon and cracked eggs into the pan, he chatted with her over his shoulder.

'I was real sorry about your dad. We all miss him a lot around here. Had a great turn-out at the funeral, though. Too bad you had to miss it.'

'Yes, it was,' she said in a tight voice. 'I was out of town when it happened, and didn't get back until it was over.'

Carl gave her a long close look, then heaved a sigh. 'He always regretted it, you know. What he did. He was wrong, and I told him so many times. He often thought about calling or writing to you, but that stiff-necked pride of his wouldn't let him do it.'

'Never mind. It's ancient history now. Besides, can you believe it? He left everything to me after all.'

'Well, that's only fair. No matter what his faults, John Cameron always tried to do the right and proper thing.'

'Yes,' she replied slowly. 'I suppose you're right.'

When she saw the look on Carl's face, she was immediately sorry for her grudging tone. 'Don't mind me, Carl,' she apologised. 'I just got in last night and am still a little dazed.'

'Well, take it from me, in his own way your father really cared about you, Anne. And he was proud of you too, the way you managed to make your own way in the world, educated yourself, got such a fine job, and never once came begging for help.'

How on earth did he know about all that? Anne wondered as Carl went to the counter to dish up her breakfast. It had always seemed to her that she was as good as dead to her father from the minute he caught her... But there was no point in rehashing that.

'Here we are, then,' Carl said, setting her plate down.

She tucked in with gusto. 'Tell me, Carl,' she said between bites, 'what's been going on around here since I've been away?'

'You probably know Victoria Poole died about a year ago.'

'Yes, I heard. I was so sorry. How is Ben taking it?'

'About what you'd expect,' Carl answered gruffly. 'At first he was like a madman. We were all afraid

he'd do himself an injury.' He shrugged. 'Then he
seemed to calm down after a while, and now he pretty
much just keeps himself to himself.'

'He always was something of a hermit.'

She debated asking Carl's advice about the interview Jerry wanted her to get. If she knew Carl he
would be as silent as the grave about it, but she didn't
dare take the chance that Ben would hear it from
someone else before she had a chance to approach
him.

She drained the last of her coffee and rose to her
feet. 'Well, thanks for the breakfast, Carl.' She hesitated, somewhat embarrassed. 'How much do I owe
you?' she finally said. 'Or shall I pay Emma at the
desk?'

He waved a hand in the air. 'Don't bother. This
one's on us. You can pay for the next one.'

'Thanks again, Carl. You've saved my life.'

With a little wave, she went back through the dining-
room to the foyer. At the front door she stopped for
a moment to put on her jacket and scarf, when it suddenly flew open, barely missing her by a few inches
and almost knocking her down.

'Oh, I'm so sorry. Did I hit you?'

Anne looked up to see a tall young woman standing
before her. Her face was reddened by the cold, her
forehead creased with anxious concern. There was
something vaguely familiar about her, but at the
moment she couldn't quite place her.

Anne smiled. 'No, you just missed me. It was my
fault anyway. I should know better than to dawdle
right in front of the door that way.'

The girl had taken off her red knitted cap and was
shaking out a thick mane of long blonde hair. 'Say,'

she said now, giving Anne a close look. 'Don't I know you?'

Anne laughed. 'As a matter of fact, I was just thinking the same thing.'

'You're Anne Cameron, aren't you? I heard you were coming back. I'm Linda Sorenson.'

Anne could only stare, wide-eyed with disbelief. 'Little Linda Sorenson?' The statuesque girl stood at least four inches taller than her own five feet six. 'I can't believe it.'

'Not so little any more. I guess ten years makes a lot of difference, especially between nine years old and nineteen.'

The girl was perfectly lovely, very tall, with a full rounded figure her tight red sweater did nothing to conceal, a creamy flawless complexion and all that gorgeous blonde hair. Anne had to wonder how two such colourless people as Edith and Carl Sorenson could have produced such a beauty, and the very next thought that crossed her mind was that she was exactly Jerry Bannister's type.

'You've been living in Seattle all these years, from what I hear,' Linda was saying now. 'Working on a magazine?'

'That's right.'

'Lucky you,' Linda said wistfully. 'I'd do anything to get out of this backwater.'

'Well, why don't you? I did.'

Linda shrugged. 'No money. No education. No talent.' She laughed. 'I sound pretty useless, don't I?'

Anne was about to comment that she was so decorative, she didn't need to be useful, but just then she heard Carl call to his daughter.

'Linda, did you get those bills in the mail?'

Linda sighed wearily. 'Yes, Pa.'

'Well, I have some typing I want you to do.'

Linda rolled her eyes and gave Anne a look full of meaning. 'I'd better go. But I hope I'll see more of you while you're here.' She lowered her voice to a whisper. 'I could use some pointers on how to get out of here.'

Anne went outside and down the steps to the street, heading for the grocery store next door for supplies. She stopped on the path out in front for a moment to button her parka, and when she looked up again she noticed the tall figure of a man, half a block away. As he came closer she could see that it was Ben Poole, and he was walking straight towards her.

She watched him as he approached, tall, his head down, a little stooped now, his massive head of golden hair turning a little grey, until he was now only a few yards away from her.

When he finally glanced up at her, she was shocked by the dull glaze in his once bright blue eyes. His face was haggard, his massive frame seemed shrunken, and a sudden rush of pity for him swept over her. He looked as though he'd been in a terrible accident or just recovered from a severe illness.

'Anne?' he said. 'Anne Cameron? It is you!' He came closer, his arms outstretched.

'Hello, Ben,' she said.

It seemed like the most natural thing in the world to be in his arms again, made her feel really at home for the first time since she'd arrived. He bent over to kiss her on the forehead, then released her and stepped back, scanning her face with an artist's careful appraisal.

He smiled. 'It really is you. You've come back. I can hardly believe it. What a wonderful surprise! When did you get in?'

She laughed. 'You mean you didn't know I was coming? Sounds like the local grapevine has broken down. I thought surely the whole island would know not only that I was coming, but the exact moment.'

A cloud passed over his face. 'Well, I stay pretty much to myself these days.'

She could have bitten her tongue out for reminding him of his loss. 'As a matter of fact,' she went on brightly, hurriedly, 'I just got in last evening.'

'And how long will you be staying?'

'Oh, that depends. I have to settle some of my father's affairs. You know, decide what to do about the house, what I want to keep, that kind of thing. I haven't even started. Arnold Pembroke is taking care of most of the details for me.'

It was on the tip of her tongue to mention the interview, but by now that project had faded into insignificance in the sheer joy of just being with him again. Besides, it was too soon. If she started pushing him right away he'd never agree to it.

She looked up to see him staring at her. 'I can't tell you how good it is to see you,' he said. 'You look wonderful, Anne.' He raised his shaggy eyebrows. 'All grown up, in fact. Very polished. Big city life seems to agree with you.'

'Oh, it has its compensations,' she said with a nervous laugh. 'As well as its drawbacks.'

She was somewhat at a loss for words, uncertain how to broach the subject, yet knowing it had to be got out of the way. She reached out and put a hand on his arm.

'Ben, I was so sorry to hear about Victoria. I would have written, but...' She shrugged, unable to explain.

'I understand,' he replied quickly. He seemed as anxious to drop the subject as she. He gave her a sad crooked smile. 'We're pretty much in the same boat, aren't we?'

For a moment she didn't understand his meaning. Then it dawned on her that he was speaking of her father, and she had to smile.

'Oh, that's hardly the same thing. My father and I weren't exactly on loving terms.'

He gave her a searching, quizzical look. 'Perhaps not,' he said at last. 'But it was a loss all the same. Perhaps more than you realise.'

To her amazement, she felt hot tears sting behind her eyelids. Maybe he was right. Or maybe it was just self-pity. She was all alone in the world now, utterly alone—father and mother both gone, her only brother killed years ago. No husband, no children, and no prospects of either. Only a career that was going nowhere.

Suddenly Anne was uncomfortably aware that they had become the object of several interested pairs of eyes. Someone jostled them passing by, and several people were staring at them.

'I think we're creating a sensation standing here in front of the whole village,' Anne said with a smile.

Ben laughed. 'Oh, it gives them something to talk about. But I agree, it's not the best place for a reunion.'

'Well, I do have some groceries to pick up. There's nothing edible at the house.'

He took her by the arm and they started walking. 'I'll just tag along with you as far as the grocery store.

Perhaps when you get settled we can get together for
a real talk. In the meantime, is there anything I can
do to help?'

'I can't think of anything at the moment. I hardly
know what needs to be done myself at this point.'

'How about coming over this afternoon, then? We
could have a cup of tea in front of the fire, just the
way we used to.'

She realised with a pang what he didn't add—'When
Victoria was alive.'

'Yes, of course,' she said hurriedly. 'What time?'

'How about three o'clock? Or is that too late? Are
you worried about walking home in the dark?'

'On the island? Of course not. Nothing could
happen to me here. And I find I still know every inch
of every path.'

'All right, then,' he said. 'It's a date. I'll see you
this afternoon around three o'clock.'

He turned from her then and walked off. She stood
there in front of the grocery store watching him until
he disappeared from view around the last shop on the
street, filled with a sense of protective love for him.
Perhaps she could heal his hurt, ease the pain of loss
for him.

By the time she'd picked up her purchases at the
grocery store, what had started out to be a fine day
had degenerated into a gusty wind and a grey sky that
was filling rapidly with black rain clouds. Just as she
reached the road that led to her house, the heavy drops
were already spattering down, and she broke into a
brisk run.

When she finally got home, the rain was coming
down so hard that she hardly noticed the car parked
out in front. It was most unusual for anyone to at-

tempt to negotiate the rutted dirt road during the
autumn rains, although Patrick Fielding had used to
have a Land Rover, very much like this one, that could
go anywhere.

Then she saw that a man was standing on the front
porch. When she recognised him, her mouth fell open
in utter astonishment. It was Jerry—the last person
she would have expected to see. He had obviously been
waiting for her under cover. She stopped dead in her
tracks for a second or two with the rain lashing against
her face, soaking her hair, then made a dash for the
porch.

'Here, let me carry that for you,' he said, reaching
for the shopping bag, which was thoroughly sodden
by now.

Without a word she handed it to him. She was
shivering from head to toe, as much from shock as
from the penetrating wet and cold, and barely able to
fish the house key out of her purse. She fumbled it
into the lock, opened the door and stepped inside the
chilly damp house, with Jerry close behind her.

Shaking out her dripping head, she turned slowly
around to face him. 'What in the world are you doing
here?' she asked.

He was grinning down at her. 'I wish you could see
yourself. You look like a drowned rat. Where shall I
put these groceries?'

She glared at him. 'I said, what are you doing here?'

He raised an eyebrow at her. 'What kind of greeting
is that?'

The old eyebrow trick only escalated her irritation.
'You've got some nerve showing up like this out of
the blue. What do you think you're doing, checking
up on me?'

The grin broadened. 'Something like that.'

'Well, I don't believe it. I simply don't believe it.'

'Well, you'd better start believing it. Now, will you please tell me where to put the groceries? This bag is beginning to leak all over me.' He gave a low wicked chuckle. 'You really are a sight. Don't you think you'd better go dry off? I can find the kitchen myself. Then I'll light a fire. It's freezing in here.'

He turned from her, heading for the kitchen, leaving her standing there speechless and dripping all over the carpet, and still shivering. Finally, she shook herself and went down the hall to her bedroom. As she stripped off her wet clothes, her one thought was how to get rid of him. He'd obviously come up here to press her about the interview with Ben, and he'd simply spoil everything.

# CHAPTER THREE

BY THE time Anne had thrown on a pair of dry jeans and heavy white pullover, dried her hair as best she could, and hung up the damp towel on the rack in the bathroom, the smell of wood smoke was filling the house. She carried her brush into the living-room to finish drying her hair by the fire. Jerry was in there, down on his haunches in front of the stone fireplace, feeding kindling into it.

'Please,' she said, walking towards him. 'Make yourself right at home.'

He swivelled his head around to look up at her. 'Thanks, I already have. It's not a bad fire, if I do say so myself.'

'Congratulations.'

He threw in a large alder log, rose to his feet and turned around to face her. 'Say, have you got anything to eat around here? I'm starved. Haven't had a bite since breakfast.'

She put her hands on her hips and gave him a look that would kill a lesser man. 'Not until you tell me what you're doing here.'

He gave her an innocent look. 'Why, to check on how you were coming along with the interview, of course. What else? When I talked to you on the telephone last night you didn't sound very enthusiastic about the project.' He grinned and shrugged his shoulders. 'I just thought I'd come up here and give you a nudge in the right direction.'

She knew it was hopeless to argue with him. By now her anger was pretty well spent anyway. She just wanted to get him out of here as quickly as possible, and she knew that if she kept on arguing with him he'd never go.

She sat down in front of the fire and started brushing her hair. 'How did you get here so fast?'

'By seaplane. I rented the car from someone named Patrick down in the village, but I don't think it's worth much. I had a heck of a time getting over that poor excuse for a road back there.'

'This is not the heart of Seattle, Jerry,' she said drily. 'We don't have such amenities as paved roads here.' City born and bred, with luck he'd get sick of the primitive conditions and go back today. 'In any case, I'm confident Patrick's Land Rover will get you back to the village in time to catch your plane back to Seattle this afternoon.'

'Oh, I'm not going back today.'

'Just how long are you planning to stay, then?' she asked in a tight voice.

'I'm not sure. It all depends. As a matter of fact I thought I might treat myself to a little holiday. Maybe do some fishing. Patrick tells me there are steelhead trout in the streams further inland, and the salmon run most of the year up here in the salt water anyway.'

Anne's heart sank slowly into her stomach. He'd wreck everything. Yet she knew that the harder she pressed him to leave, the deeper in he'd dig his heels. Somehow she'd have to make him realise that his looming presence could very well jettison all hope of the interview.

'Jerry, please try to understand,' she said, making her voice steady and calm. 'If Ben finds out you've come up here to push him into that interview, I haven't a prayer of getting it.'

He didn't say anything for several seconds. She glanced up to see him gazing pensively into the fire, his head bent, his thumbs hooked in the waistband of his jeans, and it suddenly occurred to her that this was the first time since she'd known him that she'd seen him dressed so casually. Although ordinarily he wasn't exactly a shining example of sartorial splendour, his tie perennially loosened, his clothes always a little rumpled, they were expensively tailored and fitted him well.

Today he was dressed in tan chinos and a soft rich brown woollen shirt, just the colour of his eyes, the sleeves rolled up to his elbow and unfastened at the throat. Oddly, the outfit seemed to suit him, with his slender athletic build, broad bony shoulders, narrow waist and lean hips.

Just then he turned his head slightly. Before she could catch herself, their eyes met, and a slow grin began to spread across his face.

'See anything interesting?' he drawled.

Quickly, she looked away. 'Don't change the subject. I still can't believe you really did this. Don't you have any confidence in me at all? I don't need you to come up here and baby-sit me or hold my hand.'

He got down beside her, leaned back against the sofa and crossed his long legs in front of him. 'Well, if you're really doing that well on your own, I apologise. I'll just go fishing and leave you alone. Can I take it then that you've already set things up with Poole?'

'Well, no, not yet,' she stammered. She turned and gave him a pleading look. 'Jerry, I just got here yesterday.'

'Have you even seen the guy?'

'Yes, as a matter of fact I have,' she said. 'I ran into him this morning in the village and he invited me to his house this afternoon for tea.'

He pulled the eyebrow trick on her again. 'For tea?'

She flushed. 'It's an old custom. He and his wife and I used to have tea together in the afternoon quite often in the old days.'

He leaned his head further back and folded his arms across his chest. 'Well, that's good work, Cameron. So today you'll start the interview? Do you have a tape recorder? How about the camera? Did you remember to bring it along——?'

'No, Jerry,' she broke in firmly. 'Today I do *not* start the interview. Today, if all goes well, I *might* broach the subject. That is, if you can manage to keep out of my way.'

'Well, what did you talk about today, then?'

'Oh, just old times.'

Her hair seemed to be thoroughly dry by now. She gave it one last swipe with the brush, then rose to her feet and went over to glance out of the window. The rain had stopped, and a pale sun was struggling to come out from behind the last of the clouds. The road to the village would still be virtually impassable for another hour, however, even in the Land Rover.

She turned back to him. 'I'm afraid you won't be able to negotiate that road for a while. I'll fix some lunch before you go. If you really do intend to stay on for a few days you'd better fix it up with the

Sorensons at the hotel. You can call them from here if you like. I'll get the number for you.'

She started walking towards the hall where the telephone was kept, but before she'd gone far he was calling after her.

'Actually I thought I'd stay here with you. You seem to have plenty of room and——'

'What?' she broke in. She stopped dead in her tracks and turned slowly around to face him, shaking her head. 'No, Jerry. You can't possibly stay here. It's out of the question.'

He gave her a look of honest puzzlement. 'I don't see why.'

Suddenly acutely embarrassed, she could feel her face reddening. 'Well, this is a small village. Everyone knows me here. It's also about fifty years behind the times. If it ever got out that I had a man staying here with me alone in the house the gossip would never end. You simply can't stay here, Jerry, and that's final. It would ruin everything.'

He rose slowly to his feet and stood looking down at her, a long careful look, for several long moments. 'You know,' he said at last in a deceptively soft tone, 'I thought right from the beginning of this little venture that there was more to it than met the eye. You want to know what I think?'

'No, but I'm sure you're going to tell me.'

Ignoring the dry comment, he continued on undaunted. 'I think you've still got some kind of adolescent crush on this old geezer, haven't you?'

She lifted her chin. 'He is not an old geezer.'

'He's got to be almost fifty. Probably old enough to be your father.'

'He happens to be forty-four, hardly old enough to be the father of a twenty-seven-year-old woman. And not, I might add, much older than you.'

'Hey, I'm only thirty-five, a mere boy.' He took a step towards her, eyeing her thoughtfully. 'Come on, Cameron, give. Have you got something going with this guy?'

'How could I? I've been gone for ten years and have seen him exactly once since I got back. We talked for perhaps ten minutes.'

He gave her a cool, penetrating look. 'Maybe so,' he said slowly. 'But you'll have to admit you've got him up on a pretty exalted pedestal.'

She shrugged. 'I don't know if I'd call it a pedestal. I just think he's a wonderful man.'

'In what way?'

'Well, in every way.'

'And you don't call that a pedestal?'

She spread her arms helplessly. 'What can I say? It's hard to explain. He and Victoria were always just *there* for me, for each other. They had a perfect love, yet it didn't shut out other people. I mean, both of them were enormously kind to me, especially when my mother died so soon after my brother, and everything just kind of fell apart.'

'And so you've spent all these years since searching for that kind of love.' Jerry put his chin in his hand, rubbing it thoughtfully. 'Could that be why you've never had a romance of your own?'

'No!' she said. 'Of course not. Besides, how do you know I've never had a romance?'

'Oh, I'd know, believe me.'

'I see,' she said evenly. 'You've suddenly become omniscient, is that it?'

He braced his hands on the table and leaned towards her so that his face was only inches away from hers. 'No,' he said quietly. 'I'm not omniscient, but when a woman is in love she shows it in a hundred different ways. I've never seen a sign of it in you.' He straightened up and gazed down at her. 'I thought you were just cold. You know, not interested in men.'

'If you mean because I didn't fall all over *you*—— '

He raised a hand. 'Don't be obstructive. Why do women always have to take everything so personally? I'm only trying to help you solve your problem, and right away you get huffy.'

She jumped to her feet. 'I don't *have* a problem!' she said. 'And if I did you're the last person I'd want to help me solve it.' She pointed an accusing finger at him. 'Not with your reputation.'

'*My* reputation!' he exclaimed in genuine astonishment. 'What's that got to do with anything?'

'Well, I don't see that your love life is any shining example to follow—one blonde after another. You say I've never been in love. Well, neither have you, if it comes to that.'

'You don't know what you're talking about.'

'Fair is fair, Jerry. Let's psychoanalyse your hang-ups now that you've got mine all figured out.' He opened his mouth, but she rushed on before he had a chance to get a word out. 'Haven't you ever asked yourself why you hop from one blonde to another? Surely one of them must have measured up to your exalted standards.'

'I have my reasons,' he stated loftily.

'Let's see,' she went on, ignoring him, 'maybe when you were a child some little blonde girl hurt your feelings. Maybe tattled to the teacher on you or didn't invite you to her birthday party.'

'That's enough, Cameron,' he said in a warning tone.

'Oh? I see. It's one thing to dissect my hang-ups, but when the shoe is on the other foot it pinches, doesn't it?'

They stood there, glaring at each other, neither giving an inch. Finally, she noticed his mouth beginning to twitch at the edges. It was contagious, and in the next moment they were both literally helpless with laughter.

'Truce!' he said when he'd caught his breath. 'OK?'

She nodded. 'Truce.'

Although he was still smiling, his eyes had hardened. 'Just don't you forget why I let you come here in the first place. That interview goes at the top of your list. When you get that out of the way you can pursue your own fantasies as much as you please.'

On her way to Ben's that afternoon, dressed in her best pair of grey flannel trousers, a white silk shirt and hunter green cashmere cardigan, she thought about the things Jerry had said. Could he be right? Was she so hung up on searching for the kind of perfect love the Pooles had had that she'd denied herself a real love of her own?

Even more to the point, why had Jerry bothered to go into it in such detail? In fact, why had he come up here at all? She'd assumed it was to goad her about the interview, but now somehow that explanation didn't quite ring true. It just wasn't like Jerry. He might be the most exasperating man in the world, but he wasn't stupid, and he'd trusted her on far more important assignments in the past without bothering to check on her progress. There had to be more to it than that.

Then there was his telephone call the night she'd arrived, and the odd little scene in his office, when for just a moment he seemed to be looking at her for the first time as a woman, even a desirable one. And why did he keep harping on the subject of her feelings for Ben? If she didn't know better, she'd almost think he was jealous. Then she had to laugh. Not the Jerry Bannister she knew!

Ben's house was perched high on a cliff overlooking the northern channel. Anne slowed her steps as she approached. How many times in the past she'd come down this same road to this same house! She stopped short when she came to the old shed where Ben kept his painting equipment, and cold shivers ran up and down her spine as the memory of what had taken place there rose painfully up in her mind.

It had been her last night on the island, the night she'd thrown herself at Ben so shamelessly, sobbing out her love for him. How embarrassed he must have been! And how perfectly he had handled it. If only her father hadn't come along and misinterpreted it!

Just then Ben himself appeared at the door. 'Anne,' he called. 'You're right on time. Come on inside. I just made a pot of tea and managed to talk Carl out of some fresh-baked scones and seed cake.'

'Sounds wonderful. I could use something hot right about now. I'd forgotten how cold it can get up here on the cliff.'

He nodded. 'It's that west wind blowing off the straits. Come on. I have a fire going in the studio.'

Inside, while Ben went into the kitchen to get the tea-tray, Anne took off her jacket, scarf and gloves, and began to walk slowly around the large airy room, filled with north light, where Ben did his painting, examining the canvases stacked against the wall.

Although he used to paint only rather pretty sea-scapes or island scenes, these newer pictures were all of Victoria, in different styles and poses, as though he'd been trying to bring his dead wife back to life in his work.

'Well?' he called from the doorway. 'What do you think?'

She turned around. 'I'm not sure. They're wonderful, of course, but so different from your old style.'

'Yes.' He set the tray down on the table in front of the fire. 'But an artist can only paint what he feels.' He gazed at the portrait on the easel. 'She was so beautiful, inside as well as out, that it's hard to capture her on canvas.'

'Yes, I can imagine.'

'But enough of that. Come and sit by the fire. I want to hear about what you've been doing all these years. It seems like only yesterday that you used to come around almost every day.'

'I'm afraid I made a terrible pest of myself.'

Ben gave her a warm smile. 'Not at all. You know how fond of you Victoria and I always were. Almost like our own daughter.'

'Oh, hardly that! I'm a little too old for that.'

'Well, whatever. In any case you were like a breath of fresh air, and I've missed you. Now,' he said, leaning forward and filling her cup, 'tell me all about this job of yours. Even up here in the hinterland we've read some of the articles you've written for your magazine. And very good ones they've been, too. You have a fine vivid style that makes for interesting reading.'

Anne felt very much at home in the warm cosy room, with the fire blazing, the familiar smell of turpentine, drinking tea with Ben again, and as she basked in his warm praise of her work she knew she owed it to him to be honest about the interview right from the start. And that meant that she couldn't lie to him or try to trick him. She had to tell him the truth right now and get it out of the way. She also owed it to Jerry to at least broach the subject.

Then she realised he'd just asked her a question. 'I'm sorry, Ben. What did you say?'

'I was just wondering if you've come back here to stay. Or will you go back as soon as you've settled your father's affairs?'

'That all depends,' she said slowly. 'Actually there's another reason I came back.' She laughed nervously. 'I have this slave-driving boss who wasn't going to let me come at all unless I promised ...' She shrugged. Ben was waiting, still smiling. 'Well, actually, unless I promised to try to get an interview with you,' she finished up all in a rush.

Immediately the smile faded, his face creased into a frown, and she could feel him slipping away from her. 'I never give interviews,' he said in a clipped tone. 'You must know that.'

'Yes, I do,' she assured him hurriedly. 'And I told my boss that. But he insisted that I try.'

'All right. You've tried. You can tell him the answer is no.' He stared into the fire for several seconds, his face impassive, but when he turned back to her his expression had softened. 'Not even for you, Anne.

It's out of the question. I can only work in solitude, and I can't bear prying questions about my methods, my inspiration, all that tedious artistic jargon. I'm an artist, not a personality to be put on display. Whatever the public needs to know about me they can find in my work.'

'Yes, of course,' she murmured. 'I understand.'

He was frowning down at the cup in his big hand, apparently lost in thought, and didn't speak for some time. Finally he raised his head again.

'I don't mean to sound harsh,' he said softly. 'Especially to you, Anne. It's just that I've made a hard-and-fast rule about interviews.' He smiled. 'I think the last one I submitted to was several years ago, and I ended up breaking the poor man's tape recorder. Had to replace it myself. All those blood-suckers really want is to pry into my private life, and I won't have that.'

'I wouldn't do that, Ben,' she said softly. 'In fact, the fate of empires doesn't hang on whether I do the interview or not. I only said I'd try so he'd give me the time off. I can always say you flatly refused. He can't kill me, after all, and I'm quite sure he won't fire me.'

'Well, if it helps at all, you can tell him that I can't think of anyone else I'd trust, but a rule broken is no rule at all. I hope you'll understand.' He rose to his feet. 'Now, how about another cup of tea? And you've got to try some of Carl's seed cake.'

She scrambled up out of her chair. 'No. No thanks, Ben. I still have a lot to do at the house.' She laughed. 'Dad left his papers in such a mess that it'll take me two weeks to sort it all out. You know how he was.

Never threw anything away, and hopeless about keeping his books straight.'

She hurried to the door, where she threw the scarf over her head and slipped on her gloves. 'Goodbye, Ben. And thanks again for the tea.'

'Well, if you really must run off,' he said dubiously. He opened the door for her, then put a hand under her chin, tilting it up so that she had to face him. 'No hard feelings, I hope,' he said. 'About the interview.'

She shook her head. 'No. I understand. I knew it was a dumb idea, but I'd promised my boss I'd try.'

He nodded. 'Well, I'm sure we'll see each other again before you leave. The Sorensons still hold an open house for the islanders every Friday night, and I sometimes drop in for a while. Maybe I'll see you there and we can have a longer talk.'

'Yes, I'd like that.'

He walked with her as far as the edge of the gravel path. The sun had disappeared behind a black cloud, threatening rain again, and she stopped for a moment to tie her scarf around her head.

Ben looked up at the darkening sky. 'It looks as though there's another storm coming. You'd better make a run for it before it starts coming down.'

'Yes.' She turned to him once more. 'Thanks again for everything, Ben, especially for being so understanding.'

He put his arm around her shoulders and hugged her to him. 'Thank you, Anne. You've brightened my day no end. I've been rather lonely here since Victoria died, and you're like a breath of fresh air to me. I hope to see a lot of you while you're here.'

With a little wave, she started walking fast down the path to the road. The air seemed much colder after the warmth of the house, and the landscape that had seemed so pleasant and inviting just a few hours ago now appeared bleak, even vaguely threatening.

As soon as she stepped inside the cold house, she shed her outdoor clothing and marched straight to her bedroom. What she needed was a good hot bath. She was not only soaked to the skin, but a throbbing pain had begun to settle behind her eyes.

No wonder! First Jerry's unexpected appearance, then the sticky scene with Ben about the interview. Nor had she really quite taken in yet the fact that her father was gone. She still kept expecting to see him out of the window or coming through the door.

While the bath was running, she stripped off her wet clothes. When the tub was full, she sank into it, soaped herself thoroughly, then lay there in the slowly cooling water, gradually thawing out mentally and physically, until she actually began to feel almost human.

Although the visit had been painful, it had been very good for her to return to the scene of her youthful 'crime', to get that old episode with Ben out of the way for good. Somehow just being with him again had put it all in proportion for her, made her see it for what it really was—an adolescent outburst that had done no real harm.

Except for her father's reaction, that was. But even that now seemed more understandable. He had been hurting too, losing first his son, then his beloved wife, saddled with the responsibility of a troubled young girl. Her deepest regret now was that it was too late to make it up with him, that she hadn't even tried.

However, she was very relieved to get the question of the interview settled definitively. The next time she saw Jerry she'd just have to tell him the whole thing was off. He wouldn't like it, but she would *not* let him bully her into bothering Ben with it again.

As for his story about staying around to do some fishing, that was only a fairy-tale. She should have realised it at the time. In the five years she'd known him she'd never even seen him *eat* a fish, much less catch one.

When the water was cold she got up out of the tub and reached for a towel. As she dried off, shivering again in the icy room, she started to sneeze, and her headache seemed to be escalating into an insistent throbbing pain just behind her eyes. She definitely was coming down with something.

After she'd put on her bathrobe and slippers, she hunted around in the medicine cabinet until she found an old bottle of cold capsules. Eyeing them dubiously, she carried them to the kitchen, where she debated making another pot of tea. By now she was feeling so rocky that she decided to risk the cold capsules, and perhaps a warming drink.

She rummaged around on the topmost cupboard shelf where her father used to keep his meagre liquor supply until she came across a bottle of brandy. Not her favourite, but it would have to do. She poured some out in a glass, and on the basis that if a little was good, a lot was even better, choked down two of the capsules with it.

There were still hot coals in the fireplace from the fire Jerry had built earlier. She got it going again with some crumpled-up newspaper, threw on some kindling, and soon had a nice bright fire going. She curled

up on the sofa in front of it, laid her head back, closed
her eyes and waited for the medicine to take effect.

The next thing she knew she was being shaken vi-
olently, and a loud voice was ringing in her ears.

'Anne! Are you all right? Wake up, Anne!'

Blearily she forced her eyes open and raised them
up to see Jerry leaning over her, his face white and
drawn. His hand was still on her shoulder, shaking
her. She sat bolt upright, then put her hands on her
head and groaned at the excruciating pain that shot
through it.

'Will you please quit shaking me?' she pleaded.
'The top of my head is about to come off.'

When she could squeeze her eyes open again long
enough to look up at him, his face swam before her.
She blinked several times, trying to get him in better
focus, without much luck. There was an awful
drumming sound in her ears, and she shook her head
cautiously, hoping to get rid of it, but it wouldn't go
away. With another piteous moan, she laid her head
back and closed her eyes again.

'You're drunk!' he said disgustedly.

She forced her head up at that and glared at him.
'Oh, don't be ridiculous. I've never been drunk in my
life.' She tried to get some dignity in her voice, but
her head was pounding so that she couldn't even hear
her words. She swallowed hard and made a valiant
effort to speak more precisely. 'It must be those pills
I took.'

He pointed at the bottle of brandy and the empty
glass still sitting on the table in front of the sofa where
she'd left them. 'And I suppose that's apple juice.'
He sniffed. 'Doesn't smell much like it to me.'

'Oh, I just had a few sips to wash down some cold capsules.' She looked up at him. 'Why are you here anyway? I thought you were going to——'

She broke off when it dawned on her that his eyes had dropped and were now fixed on a point somewhat lower than her face. She glanced down to see that her robe was gaping wide open, revealing the scanty sheer nightgown underneath and a good portion of full cleavage.

Hastily, she covered herself more securely. 'How did you get in here?'

'The door was unlocked, that's how I got in. Don't you know better than to——?'

'Oh, Jerry, please!' she cried. 'Please don't lecture me!' Her head felt a little better now, and when she looked up at him again he seemed to have stopped jumping around. 'Now, will you please tell me what you're doing here? It must be the middle of the night.'

'I tried to call you, and when you didn't answer I got worried.'

She had to smile. 'You?' she asked incredulously. 'Worried about me?'

'Not exactly,' he said smoothly. 'Worried about my story is more like it. Then I come in here and find you passed out in front of an open fire, the place reeking of booze...'

'Oh, stop it, please,' she moaned. 'I already explained about that.' She pointed at the bottle of cold capsules, still sitting on the coffee-table where she'd left them. 'It was those pills.'

He picked up the bottle, scanned the label, then set it back down and gave her a stern look. 'It says right on the label not to take any liquor with them.'

'Oh,' she said in a small voice. 'Does it?' He nodded. 'Well, I just felt so rotten I didn't even think to read the label. And I only had a mouthful of brandy.'

He just stood there gazing sorrowfully at her, shaking his head slowly from side to side. 'I can't believe it,' he said. 'A clever girl like you.'

She struggled to her feet and stood there for a moment, trying to get her balance, still hanging on to the back of the sofa. He reached out a hand to help her, but she shook him off angrily. When the room stopped spinning she tied her robe tighter and turned to him.

'Well, I'm sorry, but that's what I did, and now if you don't mind I'd like to go to bed. Now that you've seen I'm all right, you can just take yourself back to the hotel.'

His mouth started to twitch and his eyes crinkled in genuine amusement. 'You certainly don't look all right.'

'Well, I am. And, as scintillating as your company is, I'd really rather be alone right now. So will you please leave?'

'I'm afraid I can't do that.'

She gave him a suspicious look. 'Why not?'

'Well, Patrick needed the Land Rover, so he brought me out here and dropped me off. I don't have any way back.'

She pointed to the telephone in the hall. 'Well, you can just call Patrick and ask him to come and get you.'

'I don't know if he can. It's been pouring all evening, and that primitive road of yours was barely passable when we came.'

She realised then that the awful drumming she couldn't shake off was the sound of heavy rainfall coming down hard on the roof. Somehow, the whole thing was suddenly too much for her: the emotion-charged scene with Ben, whatever bug it was she'd caught, then, to top it all off, Jerry showing up out of the blue.

The room began to swim and a terrible bitter taste rose up in her throat. She closed her eyes and reached out a hand to break the fall she knew was coming.

# CHAPTER FOUR

THE next thing Anne knew, an arm was gripping her tightly around the waist, supporting her, easing her back on the sofa.

'Put your head down between your legs,' she heard Jerry say in a low voice. 'Come on, that's a good girl.'

She did as she was told, and although her head cleared as the blood rushed to it the nausea was only getting worse. Then she felt him pulling her to her feet. His arm came around her shoulders, holding her close to him, and she laid her head against his chest.

'Open your eyes,' he said firmly, but gently. 'Come on, now, we're going to take a little walk. That's right. One foot in front of the other. That's the way.'

He walked her slowly but inexorably, never loosening his grip on her, over to the window. With his free hand he pulled the curtain aside and raised the bottom sash. She gasped as a swift rush of cold damp air blew across her face. She started sucking in great breaths of it, and in a few minutes began to think she just might live.

'Better?' he asked softly.

She turned to look up at him and gave him a weak smile. 'Much better, thanks.'

He started leading her back to the sofa. 'Just sit down and try to relax. Put your head back. That's right. You'll be OK now.' He started walking away.

'Where are you going?' she called.

'Just going to make some coffee. Don't go away.'

She must have dozed off then because when she blinked her eyes open again there was a pot of coffee and two mugs and a plate of crackers on a tray on the table in front of her. Jerry was down on his haunches in front of the fire, tossing on another log. It blazed up, lighting his face, and a sudden rush of gratitude, even affection, rose up in her at the sight.

Although it had been embarrassing to be caught like that in such a state and he'd had some fun at her expense, he had handled the situation perfectly. The fleeting thought crossed her mind that he was probably used to dealing with problem women, with that long string of blondes behind him.

He rose to his feet then, and came to sit beside her. 'Feeling better?' he asked with a smile.

She nodded. 'Yes, much.'

It was true, and as she watched him pour out two steaming mugs of coffee, his large hands steady and sure, it suddenly seemed very important to her that his good opinion of her hadn't been damaged by what he'd seen tonight. She glanced over at him.

'Jerry, you do believe me, don't you? I mean, about the pills. I admit it was a stupid thing to do, mixing them with the brandy, but I really wasn't drunk.'

'I know that. Here,' he said, handing her a mug. 'Drink this. The caffeine should neutralise both the pills and the brandy.' He picked up the brandy bottle and examined it. 'Next time choose a better brand. This cheap stuff will give you trouble every time.' He set the bottle down and grinned at her. 'In fact, you'll probably have a hell of a hangover tomorrow.'

She made a face at him. 'Thanks a lot.'

She drained her coffee in just a few swallows, and it wasn't long before the caffeine did its work. She reached for a cracker and took a cautious bite to see how it would go down. It tasted so good that she finished it and reached for another. Getting food in her stomach seemed to help. She hadn't eaten anything since the scones she'd had at Ben's.

'Now,' Jerry said, leaning back with one arm stretched across the back of the sofa, 'tell me how you made out with Ben Poole today.'

'Not too well, I'm afraid.' She swallowed the last of the coffee in her mug, set it down on the tray and turned to him. 'I did ask, Jerry, honestly.'

'And he wasn't receptive?'

She shook her head. 'To say the least. In fact, he turned me down flat. Wouldn't even discuss it.'

He eyed her thoughtfully. 'Just how hard did you try?'

'What do you mean? I asked him. I even put it as a personal favour, but he got quite huffy, said he never gave interviews and I should know that. Really, Jerry, I did everything I possibly could to convince him.'

It wasn't exactly a lie, she thought. She'd certainly done all she *intended* to do. No interview was worth jeopardising her relationship with Ben. If she had pressed him, he might have refused to see her ever again, even as a friend.

Jerry was gazing thoughtfully at her, his mouth pursed, the dark eyebrow raised, scepticism etched in every feature. 'Why is it, Anne,' he asked softly, 'that I don't quite believe you?'

She looked away. 'Probably because you have such a suspicious nature,' she mumbled.

'You know, I'm determined to get that story,' he went on, ignoring the comment. 'And I think you owe it to me to tell me right here and now if you don't

think you can do the job, maybe for personal reasons.
I mean, if it's really impossible, I won't hold it against
you. There have been good stories even I haven't been
able to get. But I keep having this funny feeling that
there's something you're not telling me.'

She looked down at her hands, which were twisting
in her lap. He was right. For all his faults, his unreasonable demands, his blithe assumption that, since
the magazine was the most important thing in his life,
it should come first with all his employees, he'd been
a pretty good boss—open, above-board, fair-minded.
And he'd really been rather sweet tonight, taking care
of her the way he had.

'All right, Jerry, I'll try to explain, if you really
want me to. But I don't know if you can understand.'

'Try me.'

She nodded. 'When I first asked you for the time
off to come up here, you said you'd never heard me
mention my father. Well, when I left the island ten
years ago, when I was barely eighteen, it was because
he and I had a flaming row. I won't go into the reasons
for it now, but the upshot of it was we simply broke
off relations with each other. Now he's gone, and we
can't ever be reconciled, and I felt terrible about that.
But today, just being at Ben's again, just talking to
him, laid those old ghosts to rest. It helped a lot.' She
shrugged. 'It's probably true that Ben has always been
my ideal of what a man should be. I'd almost forgotten there were men like him in the world. He's
simply a wonderful friend. And I don't want anything to spoil it.'

She waited for some response from Jerry. He didn't
say anything for a long time, just sat gazing into the
fire. Finally he got up and threw on another log, then

came back to stand before her, looking down at her pityingly and shaking his head slowly from side to side.

'Anne, Anne,' he said softly. 'He's an old man. He's not for you. You're young, alive, a vibrant, lovely woman. You deserve better than a reclusive artist who would only feed off your youth.'

She gave him a startled look. 'Oh, you've got it all wrong.' She smiled. 'I admit that when I was a girl I had a terrific crush on him. But there's never been any question of anything like that between us. Not seriously.'

He quirked an eyebrow at her. 'Are you sure? I wonder if that old adolescent crush isn't being revived.'

'Jerry, you don't know anything about it,' she said softly. 'You don't know him. You don't really know me.'

'Oh, yes, I do,' he said. 'And, from everything you've said about the whole subject so far, it sounds very much to me as though you're looking for your father in Ben Poole.'

She could only stare at him. Although his words stung, the look he was giving her was full of genuine concern, real caring, not like the old arrogant, tyr-annical, self-centred Jerry she thought she'd known so well all these years.

Suddenly it was all too much for her. Tears of exhaustion began to sting behind her eyes, and before she could stop them they had spilled over and were now coursing silently down her cheeks. She jumped to her feet and turned away from him and covered her face with her hands.

There was dead silence in the room except for the crackling of the fire and the rain still drumming on the roof. In a moment she felt his presence behind her, his hands on her shoulders. With a loud sniff she tried to shrug him off, but he hung on, the hands moving now in a soothing kneading motion. He pulled her back against his chest and began stroking her hair, his warm breath at her ear.

'I'm sorry, Anne,' he murmured. 'Don't cry. Please don't cry. I can't stand to see you cry. Come on now. I'm truly sorry. It's all right.'

As she listened to his halting, totally ineffectual attempts to comfort her, the whole thing began to take on a humorous aspect, and in spite of herself she found the tears turning to laughter. This was hard, tough-minded, iron man Jerry Bannister, actually petting and soothing her as though he really cared.

She reached in the pocket of her robe for a tissue, and when she couldn't find one she sniffed loudly again. Then she heard his low chuckle from behind her, and she turned around to see him grinning at her, holding out a handkerchief.

'Here, you'd better blow your nose. It's dripping.'

'It's not funny,' she said stiffly. She yanked the handkerchief out of his hand, wiped her eyes, and blew her nose.

'No,' he said. 'I suppose not—at least not to you. But you should see yourself from where I stand.' He shook his head, looking her up and down. 'You look exactly like a ten-year-old whose favourite doll just got broken.'

Tears threatened again as a wave of sheer exhaustion passed over her. 'Jerry,' she said wearily, 'I'm so tired

I could drop. Please don't badger me any more
tonight.'

He didn't say anything for a few moments, then in
one swift movement he reached out for her, swooped
her up in his arms and started carrying her out of the
room. She was too tired to protest. All she could do
was put her arms around his neck and lay her head
on his shoulder.

They went down the dark hall until he came to her
bedroom. He stumbled over the clothes she had left
lying on the floor earlier, cursed under his breath, and
clutched her a little tighter so that she wouldn't fall.
By now, away from the light and the bright glow of
the fire, Anne was almost asleep. It made her feel so
safe, so protected, to be held in these strong arms.
He carried her so lightly, as though she were a feather,
a small wounded bird. A delicious sensation of
warmth filled her whole body, and she nuzzled closer
against his shoulder, bony, solid, and well-muscled.

He stood at the side of the bed for a moment, still
holding her. She could feel his warm breath on her
face, his hair brushing against her cheek, smell the
scent of his skin, fresh and clean, with just a hint of
a lemony masculine soap. She suddenly knew he was
going to kiss her, but before the idea had clearly
formed in her groggy mind his lips had come down
on hers.

In the shock of that sudden contact, she simply
reacted. Her lips parted softly under his, and when
his arms tightened around her she could feel his heart
pounding next to hers. Then carefully, his mouth still
on hers, he lowered her to her feet. Still too dazed to
take in what was happening to her, except that it felt

wonderful, she clung to him, running her fingers into the thick hair that curled at the back of his neck.

'Anne,' he whispered. His hands were moving up and down her back now.

'Mmm?' she murmured drowsily, and pressed herself up against his lean hard body.

Somehow, in transit from the living-room, her robe had come untied, and she felt his hands slip underneath it, warm and large and slightly callused on her bare back, still moving, travelling now up over arms, her shoulders, to the base of her neck. He kissed her again, harder this time, and as his hot tongue pushed past her lips one hand moved from her throat to cover her breast.

The flimsy material of her nightgown sliding over her bare skin and the touch of his fingers on the hardened peak of her breast set up an ache in her loins she'd never felt before. It never occurred to her to protest. Whatever it was he was doing, it felt so heavenly that she never wanted it to stop.

It wasn't until the hand slipped underneath the low bodice of her nightgown and began to move back and forth, stroking each breast gently in turn, and she became aware of his own hard arousal, pressed tightly against her thigh, that it penetrated her dim consciousness what was really going on here.

With a stifled little cry, she tore her mouth away from his and stepped back from him. She didn't know what to do, what to say. Would she have to beat him off bodily? Here she was, virtually stranded at the back of beyond with no other soul within half a mile, all alone with a man who was fast reaching the point of no return. She couldn't see him in the pitch-darkness, but she could hear his heavy rasping breath, feel the strong hands still gripping her bare shoulders.

Instinct told her to stand perfectly still and not say a word. In just a few seconds his breathing steadied, the hands on her shoulders relaxed and he was pushing her down gently on the bed. Was this going to be it, then? Would he take her by force? Should she, like the Victorian ladies, close her eyes and think of England?

Then she felt him tugging the blankets back. She raised her hips and slid in between the sheets. He tucked the covers under her chin, and the next thing she heard was his slow, steady tread as he walked out of the room, and the door closing behind him.

With a groan, she turned over on her stomach, buried her head in the pillows, and in two seconds was fast asleep.

Anne's first thought on awakening the next morning was that she'd just had a terrible nightmare. It must have been. It couldn't possibly have actually happened that way. She'd been overwrought, caught a cold, taken those awful pills.

Then there came drifting into her room the distinct aroma of bacon frying and the sound of a surprisingly pleasant baritone voice, albeit a little off-key, singing some spritely operatic aria, apparently in Italian.

She sat bolt upright in bed, staring wildly and clutching the covers tightly up over her shoulders. Her head started throbbing immediately. It hadn't been a nightmare! She squeezed her eyes shut tight, as though to blot out the memory.

Then she heard footsteps coming down the hall towards her room, along with the singing, which was much louder now and reaching a dramatic crescendo right outside her bedroom door. Then it flew open and Jerry strode inside, beaming. Anne pulled the covers more securely around her neck.

'Good morning, merry sunshine,' he chirped gaily. 'And how are we feeling this morning? Head any better? Not so good?'

'Go away,' she intoned slowly and distinctly.

She gave him a baleful look. He was grinning widely from ear to ear, and as he came closer she could see that not only was he wearing one of her mother's old aprons, he was also freshly shaven and had on a clean shirt. He'd obviously come prepared to stay a while.

She pointed an accusing finger at him. 'You lied to me,' she said. 'You meant to stay all along. You never intended to call Patrick to take you back to the hotel.'

'And aren't you glad I did?' he said, nodding piously. 'I saved your life last night. Come on, drink this.' He handed her a glass of orange juice.

She flopped her head back down on the pillow and looked away. 'I don't want any.'

'Oh, come on, don't be such a poor sport.' Still she wouldn't look at him or answer him. 'Anne,' he said softly. 'Look at me, Anne.'

Grudgingly she shifted her eyes sideways to see a dead serious expression on his face. 'What is it?'

He shook his head. 'Nothing happened, Anne. Promise. Nothing much, anyway. You were sick, I made you some coffee, and then I tucked you in bed. That's all there was to it.'

She gave him a dubious look. 'Promise?'

'Yes, I promise. Come on now. Just drink this.'

She finally took the glass from him and drank it down in one long gulp. It tasted like manna from heaven, and when she was finished she began to feel better right away. She handed him the empty glass and muttered an ungracious thanks. He took it and started towards the door.

'Breakfast is almost ready,' he said when he reached it. 'Bacon and pancakes.'

'I'm not hungry, Jerry, honestly.'

'Come on, it'll do you good.' He picked up the robe at the foot of the bed and threw it at her. 'I'll give you two minutes, then I'm coming back to get you.'

With a cheery wave, he disappeared from view. After he was gone she felt so much better that she had to smile. This was a Jerry Bannister she'd never known existed. What had happened to the snarling, tyrannical master of all he surveyed she'd been so used to dealing with at the office? Actually, she'd thought he'd be so angry at her for flubbing up the interview with Ben that she'd half expected him to fire her.

Now here he was playing nursemaid to her. As long as he was prepared to wait on her, she thought philosophically as she shrugged into her bathrobe and slippers, she might as well take advantage of it. In the bathroom she ran a brush through her hair, threw some water on her face and brushed her teeth. As she did so, she noticed sitting on the counter some very masculine toiletry articles—shaving gear, toothbrush, aftershave, a pair of horn-backed brushes—and she rolled her eyes heavenwards. When it came to brass, you couldn't beat the man, that was for sure.

In the kitchen he'd made an unholy mess. It looked as though every bowl, every dish, pot, pan and utensil was either sitting on the tiled counter or stacked in the sink, not to mention the food. Apparently he was the kind of cook who didn't believe in interrupting his culinary efforts to clean up after himself.

'Sit down,' he said with a gracious sweep of his hand. 'I'm just dishing it up.'

Averting her head from the litter strewn about her, she pulled out a chair and sat down. Through the window she could see that it was still raining outside, a steady drip that covered the window-pane with streaks of water. The road to the village would still be impassable, and that meant she was stuck with him at least for a while. Unless she could talk him into walking back to the hotel in the rain.

'Ah, here we are,' he announced, setting a plate before her.

She looked down at the charred bacon, limp pancakes and greasy egg, and her stomach turned over. She glanced up at him, and he gave her a defensive look.

'Well, that's the best I could do with what you had on hand.' He sat down opposite her. 'I must say you don't keep your cupboards very well stocked. We're going to be living on canned soup for a while until we can get to the grocery store.'

She poked at the yolk of her egg, hard as a rock. 'You'll be glad to get back to the hotel, I'm sure. Carl is a wonderful cook.' She took a bite of egg and was surprised to find that it didn't taste half bad.

'Oh, I'm not going back to the hotel.' He waved at the window. 'The road must still be closed.'

'You could walk.'

He nodded. 'I could, but I'm not going to.' He pointed his fork at her. 'Fun is fun, Anne, but I sent you up here to get a story out of Ben Poole, and I'm not leaving until you do. I'll get it myself if I have to.'

She bridled at his calm assumption that he was calling all the shots here. 'In case you'd forgotten, this is *my* house, and I think I have something to say about it. I told you last night that I didn't want the village gossiping about me.'

'I don't think you're worried about the village at all. You just don't want Ben Poole to find out I'm here.'

There was too much truth in that statement to argue with him. 'Just why are you here, Jerry?'

To her amazement he dropped his eyes and a faint flush spread across his face. 'I already told you,' he muttered. 'I suspected from the way you resisted the whole idea of the interview right from the beginning that your heart wasn't in it.'

'Jerry, I *tried*!' she exclaimed heatedly. 'I asked him yesterday. He turned me down flat.'

He eyed her over his coffee-cup. 'I've never known one refusal to stop you before.'

'Well, this is different!'

'I know that. And that's why I'm here.'

It was clearly time to appeal to his better nature. 'Jerry, this is important to me. Ben is an old friend. I just don't want him to get the wrong idea about— about us. What real difference does it make whether we run a story about him in the magazine?'

'Do you really care that much about what he thinks?'

'Yes. Yes, I do.'

He propped one elbow on the table, rested his chin in his hand and gazed at her. 'Anne, to my knowledge you've never had a love-affair, haven't even come close. Now it sounds very much to me as though you're falling hard for an old geezer twice your age. I can't believe it.' He grinned. 'My cool, efficient little Anne?'

'I'm not *your* anything!' she retorted. 'Now will you please just mind your own business and keep your dumb opinions to yourself? And quit calling him that! I already told you, he's just a good friend, someone who really cares about me, and I don't want anything to spoil that.' She spread her arms wide, searching for the words that would make him understand. 'The way I've always felt about Ben is something so deep, so pure, so—oh, I don't know—almost spiritual, in a sense.' Her shoulders slumped. 'I can't explain.'

'Well, I hate to bring up a touchy subject, but just let me remind you that last night your reaction to me wasn't quite as exalted as all that.'

Anne's face went up in flame. 'You said yourself nothing happened. And even if it did, you took advantage of me in my weakened condition. Besides, what do you want me to do? Bleach my hair blonde and grow a couple of inches so you can add me to your list of conquests?' She laughed harshly. 'I'm not your type, Jerry. And you certainly aren't mine.'

He didn't say anything for a long time, just sat there staring down at his plate. Finally he raised his head and looked at her, his face grave. 'And just what do you actually know about my love life, Anne? Aside from office gossip, that is.'

Anne was startled at his dead serious tone, and suddenly curious. 'To tell you the truth,' she said slowly, 'not much. I mean, do you have a family? A mother, a father, brothers, sisters? I don't even know where you live, or what you do in your spare time.

Aside from chasing blondes, that is,' she finished
tartly. 'Or,' she added with a smile, 'warding them
off, whichever the case may be.'

'See? That's what I mean. Isn't it possible that the
reason you don't know anything about me is because
you just haven't taken the trouble to find out?'

'Well, yes, I guess it could be. All right, then, tell
me.'

'About my family or about the blondes?'

'Let's start with your family,' she said in a dry tone.
'I presume you have—or had—parents.'

'Oh, yes. Both. They have a farm in Yakima, east
of the mountains from Seattle, mainly planted in or-
chard—you know, apples, pears, peaches.'

She goggled at him. 'You grew up on a farm? I can
hardly believe it!'

'See? You didn't even realise that I was just a
country boy at heart. I also have a younger brother
who loves farming as much as I detest it. He and his
wife and two children live in the old family house with
my mother and father.'

'I know what you mean about farm life,' she said
with feeling. 'My father was hooked on it, too. In
fact, sometimes I thought he cared more about his
sheep than he ever did about——' She broke off
quickly. 'But that's another story. So, how did you
escape?'

He laughed. 'I just left. They were very understanding about it, especially since Jack wanted to stay.
I got out of there as soon as I finished school and
went east to college. Columbia has a marvellous
school of journalism. Then I worked on various
newspapers and magazines in New York until I felt I
knew the business well enough to strike out on my

own. I used the money the family paid me for my
interest in the farm to buy my first magazine.'

'You were very young to become such an
entrepreneur. You had to be well under thirty.'

He shrugged. 'It was a young magazine. In any
event, it was a success, so I just went on from there.
And when I bought the magazine in Seattle seven years
ago, I decided I liked the place well enough to stay
permanently.' He braced his hands on the arms of his
chair, rose to his feet and started clearing the table.
'And now that you know my life history, I think I'd
better wash up.'

She carried her dishes to the counter and started
putting food away. As they worked silently side by
side, she mulled over the things he had told her about
himself. They had revealed an entirely different Jerry
Bannister from the one she thought she had known,
and a much more likeable one at that.

He rinsed off the dishes carefully then ran water
into the bowl and started washing them. She got out
a tea-towel and began to dry. The whole scene gave
her an odd sense of unreality. Here they were, in the
kitchen of her old home, the last place she'd ever expected to be again at all, much less with her boss at
her side up to his elbows in soapy water. She gave him
a sideways glance, her curiosity about him still not
satisfied.

'There is one thing I've often wondered,' she said,
breaking the silence.

He turned to her. 'What's that?'

'Why you've never married. Haven't you even been
tempted?'

An expression of sheer horror crossed his face.
'Lord, no,' he spluttered. 'Women today don't want

to be wives and mothers. They're all too busy with their careers and finding themselves.'

'You mean,' Anne replied sweetly, 'the way men have always been?'

'All right, you've got a point. Women have a perfect right to compete in what used to be a man's world. I have no problem with that. But that doesn't change the facts. So long as women want the same thing men do, including sexual freedom, I see no point in settling down with just one of them. Take a look at the divorce statistics. Do you have any idea what that does to children?' He shook his head firmly. 'I don't want any part of it.'

She was searching her mind for a cogent rebuttal when there came a loud knocking at the front door. Anne's heart plunged into her stomach.

'Oh, lord,' she groaned. 'Who could that be?'

Jerry started to dry his hands. 'I'll go.'

'No, you won't,' she replied firmly. 'You stay right where you are. Don't even show your face.'

Tying her robe tighter, she ran out of the kitchen and through the living-room to the front hall. At the door she paused a moment to run her fingers through her hair, then took a deep breath and pulled it open. There, standing on the other side, to her utter horror, was Ben Poole.

'Ben!' she said.

She stood there gaping at him, her mind racing, in an agony of indecision. On no account did she want him to come in and find Jerry, but she couldn't leave him standing out there on the porch.

'I'm sorry to disturb you so early, Anne,' he said. 'And I can't stay. I just got word that the road to the village is washed out completely and the telephone cable is broken. I came over to let you know and to see if you needed anything.'

'Oh, thank you, Ben, but I don't think——' She broke off then when she saw his eyes shift and move past her, a puzzled look on his face.

'I'm sorry,' he said stiffly. 'I didn't know you had company.'

# CHAPTER FIVE

FEARING the worst, Anne turned around slowly to see Jerry strolling towards them. She tried to signal him with her eyes to back off, but he kept on coming, a broad grin on his face, making straight for Ben, his hand outstretched in greeting, looking for all the world like a benign host.

'Mr Poole?' he said. 'What a pleasure it is to meet you at last.'

Ben gave Anne a bewildered look, then took Jerry's hand and allowed him to pump it vigorously. 'How do you do, Mr——?'

'Bannister,' Jerry supplied immediately. 'Jerry Bannister.'

'Mr Bannister. I just came over to tell Anne that the road was washed out and see if she needed anything.' He turned to her. 'If not, then I guess I'll be on my way.'

'Oh, don't run off,' Jerry said, opening the door wider and beckoning Ben inside. 'At least have a cup of coffee before you go. We were just finishing breakfast and I have a fresh pot of coffee on the stove.'

Ben hesitated, glancing from Jerry to Anne and back to Jerry again. 'I don't know...'

By now Anne was in an agony of embarrassment over Ben's catching her with her bathrobe still on, but, what was worse, what he'd think about Jerry's unexplained presence in the house. She was also ready to crown Jerry for the way he was choreographing the whole scenario. It was time she took charge.

She stepped between the two men. 'I'm sure Ben has things to take care of at home. Don't you, Ben?'

Jerry nudged her aside. 'I've wanted to meet you for a long time, Mr Poole. How about just one quick cup? You look as though you could use it, and I'd be grateful for a chance to discuss your work with you.'

Ben's ears had perked up at the mention of Jerry's interest in his work, which Anne knew was a total fabrication. 'Well, all right,' he said. 'One cup.'

He stepped inside and Jerry closed the door after him. As he led Ben past Anne over to the sofa, he gave her a look full of meaning. 'Maybe you'd better go check on the coffee, Anne,' he suggested. 'We don't want it to boil over.'

'No,' she said through her teeth. 'We wouldn't want that.'

It was hopeless. Unless she wanted to create a scene, she'd just have to go along with his little charade. Clearly he wasn't going to budge an inch. In the kitchen, as she'd suspected, there wasn't the slightest sign that Jerry had even begun to make a pot of coffee. With a sigh, she emptied the used grounds, filled the pot and set it on the stove.

Still seething, she marched down the hall to her room to get dressed. Of all things to happen! What must Ben think? She'd have to find a way to set him straight. That dratted Jerry! Just when she was beginning to like him, he had to pull a dirty trick like this. When she was dressed, her hair combed more carefully, a dash of powder and lipstick applied, she went back to the kitchen, where the coffee was just about to boil over.

From the living-room she could hear the low murmur of voices. She filled the mugs, set them on a tray, and carried it over to the door, then stood there quietly for a second, straining to make out what they were saying. It was Jerry's low baritone she heard first, and she almost dropped the tray, hardly able to believe her ears.

'What impresses me most about your work, Ben,' he was saying in low earnest tones, 'is that in my opinion, at least, you've somehow succeeded in making that leap from the nineteenth-century Impressionists to the modern age that the abstract painters have ignored. You're the bridge between Van Gogh, Renoir, Degas, and, say, Klee or Picasso.'

'It's odd that you should say that, Jerry,' Ben replied. 'That was exactly my intention, my original inspiration.'

She'd heard enough. What Jerry knew about painting she could put in her eye. Now it looked as though he was well on the way to soft-soaping Ben into an interview she herself had failed to get, and all her reporter's instincts were aroused.

She carried the tray into the living-room and set it down on the table. Jerry was busily feeding the fire, and Ben was sitting on the sofa, leaning forward in concentration, his blue eyes alight with the pleasure of discussing his work with someone who seemed to know what he was talking about.

'Here we are,' she said pleasantly. She handed the two men their mugs, then sat down next to Ben. 'Ben, I suppose Jerry has already mentioned the fact that he's my boss.'

'Why, no,' Ben said in surprise.

'Oh, yes,' she went on. 'He's the head man at the magazine I work for.' She laughed lightly. 'You know, the slave-driver I told you about yesterday. He's the one who sent me up here to try to get the interview with you, remember?'

'I see,' Ben said slowly. 'Somehow I had the impression he had something to do with a gallery or museum, or was an art critic.'

'I wonder what gave you that idea?' she asked with her most innocent air.

She could feel Ben tense beside her, saw the sharp look he darted at Jerry. 'If this is about the interview...'

Jerry waved a hand in the air. 'Of course it's not about the interview. When Anne told me she'd asked you and you'd turned her down, I understood perfectly.' He flashed a boyish grin. 'And I can't say I blame you. I only wanted the chance to meet you, to discuss your work with you. That's all.'

Although Ben still eyed him warily, he did seem to relax a little. 'As I told Anne yesterday, there's nothing personal in my refusal. It's just that I've made it a rule never to talk to reporters. All they want is gossip about my personal life, and since my wife died...'

Jerry sat himself down on the other side next to Ben. 'I realise that's a painful subject for you, Ben, but it is true, isn't it, that it was after you lost your wife that your work changed so dramatically? In fact, she's the subject of almost all your paintings since then, isn't she?'

Ben nodded. 'Yes, or my memories of her.'

'She must have been a very beautiful woman, inside as well as out,' Jerry said softly. 'Your portraits of her leave one in no doubt that you loved her very much.'

Anne listened, dumbstruck, at this exchange. The blasted man was going to get that interview! *Her* interview! How did he do it? He was a magician. Here he had poor Ben eating out of his hand. He seemed to know exactly what to say to him, how to draw him out, and all without rousing the least suspicion that that was what he was doing.

Finally, Ben finished his coffee and rose to go. The two men shook hands, still totally ignoring Anne, who could only stand by helplessly watching them as they walked together to the door. The crowning blow came as Ben stepped outside.

'By the way, Ben,' Jerry said in his most casual tone. 'Would it be all right if I wrote up a short piece on our conversation today? Nothing about your personal life, I promise. Only the work itself, and you'll have complete right of approval before it's printed.'

'I don't know,' Ben said slowly. Then he smiled. 'Sure. Why not?' He looked past Jerry then to wave at Anne. 'See you later, Anne. If you need anything, let me know.'

'Thanks, Ben,' she said in a tight voice. 'I will.'

When he was gone, Jerry closed the door behind him and turned around to face her. At the sight of the smug, insufferable grin of self-satisfaction on his face she had to make a heroic effort not to pick up her mug and throw it at him.

She crossed her arms over her chest and gave him a withering look. 'You're some piece of work,' she said in a low voice throbbing with emotion.

He came walking jauntily towards her. 'I don't know what you're complaining about. I got the story, didn't I?'

She pointed an accusing finger at him. 'You *tricked* him into giving it to you!' she cried. 'Poor Ben never knew what hit him!'

He narrowed his eyes at her. 'Why "poor Ben?" Will Ben be hurt by it? In any conceivable way? All artists have an enormous streak of arrogance. They have to, or they wouldn't be able to create at all. And they all crave recognition—it's only human. I just provided Ben a painless way to get it.'

She had to admit he had a point, but she was still angry at the underhanded way he'd done it. 'All that falderal about Van Gogh and Degas! You wouldn't know a Michelangelo from a Peanuts cartoon.'

'Homework, my dear,' he intoned pedantically. 'First rule of journalism. Always do your homework. While you were up here making cow eyes at the man, I was boning up on the art world.' He sat down. 'Come on now, we have work to do. I want to get it all on paper while it's still fresh in my mind.'

'Just tell me one thing. Did you really mean it when you told him you'd give him the right of approval before you printed it?'

His eyes widened in surprise. 'Of course I did. I said so, didn't I? Listen, I want success as much as the next person, but I have to live with myself, and I always play fair with my subjects. I have nothing but contempt for reporters who gain a person's confidence, then betray it. Now let's get busy. You find a notebook or something and I'll dictate the gist of my conversation with him while it's still fresh in my mind.

Then later you can fill in the background dope yourself—you know, for colour.'

There was no arguing with the man. With a sigh Anne went over to her father's desk and began searching through the mess for something suitable to write on. As she pawed through all the old bills, bank statements, Christmas cards, letters, it occurred to her with a pang that she still had to clear all this debris away.

Finally she came upon the notebook where he'd kept all the records for his sheep—vaccinations, breeding-time, lambing. As she turned over the pages, covered with her father's near-indecipherable scrawl, a strange feeling began to creep over her—half-sorrow, half-anger—and she was reminded once again that he was gone forever now.

Hastily she flipped through the used portion with unseeing eyes. There were still plenty of blank pages in the back. It would have to do. She found a ball-point pen that worked, took the book over to the couch and sat down at the table in front of it.

She looked at Jerry, who was standing a few feet away, a familiar gleam in his deep brown eyes. It struck her then how much he loved his work, and felt herself being caught up in his contagious enthusiasm.

'OK,' she said briskly. 'Ready.'

He began pacing the room, not saying anything for some time, and frowning deeply as he gathered his thoughts. He finally began to speak, haltingly at first, then, as he warmed to his subject, so rapidly that she could scarcely keep up with him.

They broke briefly for a quick lunch, still discussing angles for the story. He questioned her about Ben personally. Since the subject was such an intimate aspect of her own early life, she had no trouble filling him in on his background. Jerry would listen carefully, then either nod his approval or frown when it didn't quite fit what he wanted.

By mid-afternoon, Anne had almost filled the journal with her hastily scribbled notes. During a pause, she glanced out of the window to see that it had finally stopped raining and a pale sun was struggling to break through the remaining wispy clouds.

She leaned back and flexed her fingers. 'Jerry, I don't think I can write another stroke. Aren't we about through? We've covered every conceivable angle by now. Several times, in fact.'

He glanced down at her in surprise, his mind still a million miles away. 'Well, we want to get it right, don't we?' He thought a minute. 'Yes,' he said at last. 'You're probably right. Do you think you can get it typed up this afternoon?'

'Jerry, have a heart!' she exclaimed. 'I'm dead beat. Besides, I don't have a typewriter.'

'I do,' he responded promptly. He gave her a rather sheepish grin. 'I just happened to bring one along with me yesterday.'

'I see,' she said in a tight voice. 'You just *happened* to bring a typewriter to my house when you came to check on me. Or had you forgotten you came because you were so worried about me?'

'Tools of the trade,' he said. 'It goes everywhere with me.'

She had to laugh. It was so typical of him. In a way, she even had to admire him for his dedication. Besides, he had been kind to her last night, and even cooked breakfast this morning. Regardless of how awful it was, his intentions had been good.

'Well, right now I'm too tired to start pounding a typewriter.' She jumped up from the couch and stretched her arms high above her head to get the kinks out. 'The sun is shining. I think I'll take a short walk to clear my head, then——'

She stopped short when she saw the look on his face. His glittering dark eyes were fastened at exactly the point where her sweater strained tightly against her breasts as she stretched. She flushed deeply, then slowly lowered her arms to her sides.

He raised his head then, and their eyes met briefly. What she saw in those brown depths shook her, and there flashed through her mind the memory of the way he'd held her last night when he'd carried her to bed, the sweetness of his kiss. She arranged her sweater more loosely and turned from him.

'Anyway,' she mumbled, 'I need some fresh air. Surely the story can wait a few hours.'

'Fair enough,' he said in a perfectly normal tone of voice. 'Actually, I thought while you did the typing this afternoon I'd get some more wood chopped. We're just about out, and I could use the exercise.'

Although his bland assumption that he was staying on at the house troubled her a little, she didn't feel like arguing with him about it now. The room had suddenly come to feel very warm, almost stifling, and she only wanted to get out of there, away from his disturbing presence.

'I'll see you later, then,' she said, moving past him. 'I'll just get my things from my room, then maybe wander down as far as the crossroads to see what the road looks like by now.'

By the time she got back from her walk the clouds had completely dispersed and the sun was really quite warm, warm enough in fact for her to shed her jacket. Although the flood had receded, the road was still impassable, by car at any rate.

Jerry could walk back to the village, but he'd brought so much luggage along with him that it would be tough going. It would serve him right, she thought, except that it probably wouldn't hurt her to put him up for one more night. Since they'd just about finished the story, he might not even want to stay on at all. A man like Jerry thrived in a more cosmopolitan setting, and he was probably anxious to get back to the city, especially the nightlife.

Surely by now, since getting rid of Claudia, he must have another blonde on the string, and she had to wonder what in the world had made him come on to her last night. As she'd told him, she certainly wasn't his usual type. Propinquity, she decided as she turned into the path that led to the house. They'd been stranded here alone together, she'd been in a weakened condition, and the moment was just right. Besides, she added with a suppressed giggle, in the dark he wouldn't have noticed that her hair wasn't blonde.

As she approached the front porch she could hear a steady thud, thud coming from the back of the house. Curious, she went around the side to see what it was. When she reached the far corner, she stopped dead in her tracks and stared.

There was Jerry, stripped to the waist, her father's axe in hand, chopping wood. His back gleamed with perspiration and his dark hair was falling over his forehead. He was turned slightly away from her so that he couldn't see her, and she stood there for several moments watching as he raised the axe high above his head, then brought it crashing down on to the log.

She'd never realised what a strong muscular body he had. Not an ounce of fat on him, the shoulders broad, the arms strong and well developed. His jeans were riding low on his slim hips, and they seemed to slip a little lower every time he raised his arms up. Strange sensations began to course through her at the sight, so unsettling that she quickly turned away and ran back to the front of the house.

In the living-room she saw that he had set up the typewriter on the table by the sofa. With a sigh, she sat down and started in on it.

She spent the next hour trying to decipher her scribblings well enough to transcribe them on the typewriter in some kind of order, and by then had had enough for one day. She needed a bath and a change of clothes before thinking about what to scrounge for dinner among the meagre supplies she'd bought at the grocery store.

After she had her bath, she put on her silk shirt and grey flannel trousers. Then, at the mirror over the dresser, she brushed her hair carefully, teasing it a little to give it a softer look. She'd been such a mess ever since Jerry arrived that she wanted to show him she could look more attractive, more feminine, when she tried. She dabbed a little powder on her nose to take off the shine, applied some pale coral lipstick, a touch of mascara.

When she was finished, she gazed at her reflection, humming a little under her breath, quite pleased with her appearance. She'd also done a good day's work, which was always satisfying. Maybe a little perfume, she thought, reaching for the bottle on the dresser.

Suddenly she stopped short, her hand in mid-air. 'What am I doing?' she said aloud. Why was she taking such pains to look nice for Jerry Bannister? Had she turned into one of those repressed old maids who had erotic fantasies at the drop of the hat?

She'd just have to change her clothes into something more neutral immediately, scrub off the makeup, comb her hair back in its usual style, forget the perfume.

Just then she heard the back door open and close and Jerry's footsteps going through the kitchen into the living-room. It was too late. He'd come looking for her any minute, anxious to find out how far she'd gone with the typing.

She went into the living-room, where he was just dumping the logs he'd chopped into the scuttle by the hearth with a loud crash. He'd put his shirt back on but left it unbuttoned.

'Well,' she said, walking towards him, but still managing to avert her eyes from the masculine chest. 'You have been busy.'

'You're darned right I've been busy.' He straightened up slowly and stood staring fixedly at her for a while, then gave a low whistle. 'My,' he said at last. 'Don't you look——?' He faltered, fumbling for the right word. 'Nice,' he added finally. 'What's the occasion? Or did you go to all that trouble just for me?'

'Don't be silly,' she said tartly. 'I'm just so glad to get that story out of the way, I thought it was time to celebrate.'

'Ah, yes. The story. How did you make out with it this afternoon?'

'Not bad. It's still pretty sketchy, but shouldn't need much polishing. You can look it over tonight, and we can probably get it in final form by tomorrow.'

'Good work, Anne,' he said with a nod of satisfaction. 'See? I told you you could do it.'

'Yes, with your help.' She shook her head. 'I still can't quite figure out how you managed to talk him into it.'

He shrugged. 'Oh, I'm an old hand at that kind of thing.'

'Well, you probably want to clean up now after your arduous labours. The bathroom is free. I'll go see what I can find to fix for our dinner.'

As Jerry had predicted, there really wasn't much in the cupboards except cans of soup. There were still some eggs and cheese left in the fridge, however. Maybe an omelette with soup and crackers would be enough. Tomorrow, if the road was clear, she could go to the village and stock up on groceries.

As she pottered in the kitchen, she could hear Jerry moving around in the back of the house, and when the shower came on and he began to sing again she had to smile. After such an inauspicious beginning, they had ended up being quite comfortable together. She was almost sorry that it would end tomorrow. She began to picture him as he'd looked chopping wood, and gradually the image began to change to one of him standing under the shower, soaping the tall lean muscular body, rinsing off——

Suddenly she realised that the egg she was holding in her hand had been squeezed so tightly that its insides were dripping all over the counter. Cursing herself for her clumsiness, she started to mop up the mess. She'd have to pay more attention to what she was doing than that, or old eagle-eyes would get suspicious.

It wasn't until she was rinsing egg yolk out of the dishcloth that it dawned on her that it was only five o'clock. What was she thinking of anyway? It was too early to make dinner. She shook her head angrily. Where was her mind lately?

Putting the carton of eggs back in the refrigerator, she went into the living-room and switched on the lamp. The sun had gone down, it was dark out, and the house was growing chilly.

She decided to try to light a fire, not her strong point, but since Jerry had chopped all that wood she could at least make the effort. She wadded up old newspaper, lit it, then put in a handful of kindling. When it was blazing nicely, she threw a heavy log on top. With a brief puff of smoke, the flame fizzled out immediately.

She was on her knees, still trying ineffectually to coax it back into life, when she heard Jerry come in behind her. She jumped to her feet and turned to face him. He was freshly shaven, his dark hair still damp, and dressed in black trousers and a clean white shirt, open at the neck, the sleeves rolled up over his forearms.

'I never could get one of these things going properly,' she said. 'At home I use those three-hour treated logs, and even they give me trouble.'

He glanced at the smoking hearth. 'You just put the log on too soon, that's all.'

He got down on his haunches and with the fire-tongs moved the log off the kindling and set it to one side. He started feeding in more paper, blowing on it until it caught. He jabbed at the kindling with the poker, spreading it out until it too blazed up.

'Tell you what,' he said. 'I'll take care of the fire. Why don't you go see if you can find something to drink besides that awful brandy? As you said, we deserve a little celebration after our hard day's work.'

'Fair enough,' she said, relieved of the responsibility for the fire. 'But I don't know what kind of luck I'll have.'

In the kitchen she got up on a chair to explore the topmost cupboard more thoroughly. Finally, after rummaging around among the dust and the cobwebs and a few half-empty bottles of the sweet liqueurs her mother used to like, she found an unopened bottle of sherry that must have been there since time began. Her father never drank wine. It was probably a gift he'd never even bothered to open.

She got out two wine glasses, a corkscrew, and another plate of crackers, and carried everything on a tray back to the living-room. By now Jerry had a merry blaze going, and she stood there for a moment, watching the firelight play over his strong features. He really was an awfully good-looking man. Just then he turned and she held up the bottle.

'I hope you like sherry. Outside of some ancient *crème de menthe*, it was all I could find. Unless you want to risk what's left of the brandy.'

He made a face. 'No, thanks. Sherry's fine.'

She set the tray down. 'You'll have to take the cork out. I always manage to crumble them into little pieces.'

He took up the bottle, deftly removed the cork with a few twists of the corkscrew and poured out the glasses. He handed her one, then raised his and clinked it against hers.

'Here's to the story,' he said.

'The story,' she murmured.

They sat down on the couch in front of the fire and sipped their wine in a companionable silence for some time. The room seemed much cosier now, and it was very pleasant to just relax and enjoy the wine, the quiet—and the company.

Finally, he laid his arm on the back of the couch and shifted towards her. 'Well, Cameron,' he said. 'Last night you wormed my past history out of me. Tonight it's your turn. What about you?'

She smiled and waved a hand in the air. 'Oh, there's not much to tell. My mother died ten years ago and now with my father gone I don't have any family at all.'

'Ah, then you're an orphan. No brothers or sisters?'

'I had an older brother. David. But he was killed in a boating accident when he was sixteen.'

'I'm sorry,' he said softly. 'That must have been rough. Were you close?'

'Oh, yes. I adored him. But it was so long ago that I don't really think much about it any more. It almost killed my mother, though. In fact, in a way it did. She died just a few years after David did.'

'How about your father? It must have been hard on him to lose both his son and his wife that way. I'm surprised it didn't bring you and him closer together.'

She frowned. 'It should have, but he doted on his only son, of course, and worshipped my mother, and I think after they were both gone he actually resented me, just for being alive. In any case, everything simply fell to pieces that summer my mother died. I ended up leaving the island and never coming back.'

'Until now,' he said.

She darted him a swift look. 'Yes. Until now.'

'And did Ben Poole have anything to do with your leaving?'

She flushed, determined not to tell him *that* story. 'Oh, in a way. I guess I'd always been crazy about Ben. His wife was my mother's best friend and had been awfully good to me. That summer it just seemed as though my life here had reached a dead end. Everything was hopeless. My father—well, we had a kind of ugly show-down I won't go into. And Ben was certainly out of my reach.'

'But not any more.'

She swallowed the last of the wine in her glass, then refilled it from the bottle. 'I don't know, Jerry, I honestly don't know.'

He leaned back and gave her a long look. 'Well, I've already told you what I think about that situation.'

'Yes,' she agreed firmly. 'You have. And I don't really want to hear——'

'I think,' he went on blithely, ignoring the interruption, 'that you see Ben Poole as a father figure, a kind of substitute for your own father, who obviously rejected you after your mother died.'

She gave him her most withering look. 'So now you're a psychiatrist! You have it all figured out. Well, you're wrong. My feelings for Ben have nothing to do with my father.'

He shrugged. 'All right, calm down. Have it your way. I just hate to see you throw yourself away on an old——'

'Jerry,' she warned. 'If you say one more word about that, I'll never speak to you again.'

He held up a hand defensively. 'All right, all right, I won't say it.' He grinned. 'But I can think it.'

'Besides,' she went on, ignoring the comment, 'what makes you think Ben would want me?'

'Oh, he'll want you all right.'

She gave him a sharp look. 'What makes you say that?'

'Well, who wouldn't?' He stared broodingly into the fire for a few moments, then turned back to her and reached out to place a hand on the side of her face. 'Any man would be glad to get you, Anne.'

She looked into his eyes, such a deep brown that they looked almost black in the firelight. The touch of his hand had come like an electric shock, and as their eyes locked together she could feel the tension building up between them. She couldn't move. The dim room, their isolation, the wine, the discussion of her past—several things, in fact—all seemed to come together to work on her like some kind of potent drug.

'Jerry,' she said in a weak voice.

'Shh,' he said. 'Don't say anything.'

His hand slipped from her cheek to the back of her neck, pulling her gently towards him until their bodies were just touching. Slowly he bent his head and she closed her eyes, waiting. When he kissed her, softly, sweetly, an insidious warmth began to build inside her. A tiny voice in a dim corner of her mind accused her of being disloyal to Ben, but those warm seeking lips on hers felt so good that she was simply unable to resist.

His mouth left hers then and moved slowly across her cheek. He lifted her hair up and she could feel the warmth of his breath in her ear. His other hand came to rest at the base of her throat, and she knew that if she didn't do something now, right away, she'd be lost, past the point of no return.

She pulled her head away from his and forced him to meet her eyes. 'Jerry,' she said quietly, 'why are you doing this to me?'

He smiled crookedly. 'Why not? I like you. Sometimes I even think you like me.' He removed his hands, then reached over for his glass and took a long swallow of wine. 'I'll tell you something, Anne,' he said, dead serious now. 'I've had my eye on you from the day you walked into my office five years ago looking for a job. But you were always so cool and stand-offish, with that touch-me-not air of yours, that I decided not to do anything about it.'

Her eyes flew open. 'Me? You were attracted to me?'

He nodded. 'Yep. You.'

'You don't seriously expect me to believe that, do you?'

'I don't see why not,' he said in a hurt tone.

She had to laugh. 'Well, for one thing, I'm not blonde or tall and willowy, and for another you said yourself you had no intention of making a serious commitment to any woman.'

'And I suppose you'd never settle for less?'

She shook her head vigorously. 'No, I wouldn't. Pretty old-fashioned, huh?'

'*Very* old-fashioned, I'd say. In fact, archaic in this day and age.' He stared down at his hands, clasped loosely between his long legs. 'People can change,' he said at last. He looked over at her. 'If the right person came along.'

'You mean me?' She shook her head. 'I don't think so. My feelings about love and marriage, commitment to something beyond the thrill of the moment, run pretty deep.'

'No,' he said quietly. 'I meant me.'

'Oh, you'll never change, not a chance.' She laughed. 'You're too successful at the way you operate now.'

'You could take that chance. You know, Anne, you can't play it safe all your life.'

'I can try.'

He gave her a quizzical look. 'And do you think someone like Ben Poole would give you what you want? Marriage? I suppose children?'

'Well, he's pretty old-fashioned, too.'

'Don't you think he might be a little old to be starting a family?'

'Jerry,' she said in a warning tone. 'Don't start.'

With a heartfelt sigh he rose abruptly to his feet and stood for a moment looking down at her. 'Too bad,' he murmured. 'We could have had some good times together.'

Looking up at him, she had to admit to herself that she was more tempted than she would have dreamed possible. It was true. Even a brief fling with a man like Jerry would be an experience to remember, something to tell her grandchildren about—if she ever had any.

He reached out and took her hand and pulled her up. 'Now, I'm starved. Did you find anything edible in that kitchen besides soup?'

# CHAPTER SIX

THE next morning Patrick showed up around ten-thirty in the Land Rover just as Jerry was finishing his last red-pencilled revision to Anne's draft story.

'I figured you folks might need a lift into the village after being stranded out here for two days.'

'That's very thoughtful of you, Patrick,' Anne said. 'I appreciate it.'

The three of them were sitting at the kitchen table drinking coffee. It was another fine day, bright and sunny, without a cloud in the sky. Patrick Fielding had been a great crony of Anne's father, had known her since she was born, and local legend was that he had been in love with her mother before her marriage—and, according to some people, even afterwards.

He was a stooped, rather taciturn man, with a thinning head of grizzled hair and a ruddy face, seamed and weathered by a lifetime spent outdoors on the sea. His wiry frame appeared somewhat scrawny, but he was as tough and strong as leather.

'Any chance I can borrow the Land Rover for a couple of hours?' Jerry asked. 'Or will you be needing it all day?'

Patrick reached under his red woollen cap and scratched his head thoughtfully for a minute. 'No,' he said finally. 'I guess you can have it for a while.'

'Great,' Jerry said. 'I have some errands to run, but they won't take long. Of course,' he added quickly, 'I'll be glad to pay you for the use of it.'

Patrick gave him a hurt look. 'No need for that. You can fill the tank with petrol if you want.'

Jerry smiled apologetically. 'Of course. Whatever you say.'

The old fishermen swallowed the half-cup of coffee he had left in one long gulp, then rose to his feet. 'Guess I'll go wait outside. The fan belt's been flappin' around lately and I need to tighten it.' He looked at Anne. 'You be ready to leave in, say, half an hour?'

'Oh, yes,' she replied. 'That's plenty of time.'

When he was gone, Anne glanced over at Jerry, who was sitting opposite her gazing abstractedly after Patrick. Since she'd used the last of the eggs in last night's omelette, they'd only had a sketchy breakfast of toast and coffee, so there wasn't much clearing away to do. After that they'd been so absorbed in going over her story that they hadn't had time for any personal chat.

It was just as well, she thought now as she watched him covertly from under half-closed eyelids. She'd hardly slept a wink all night, tossing and turning, her mind in a turmoil over what had happened between them last evening.

He'd implied—no, he'd actually come right out and *said*—that it was possible for him to change. For her. Did he mean it? Or was it only part of his strategy to sweet-talk her into bed? Which he clearly wanted to do. In spite of his colourful reputation, she was more flattered than she'd realised at first by his desire for her, and she had to admit that she was attracted to him.

Living at such close quarters with him these past few days, marooned by the floods, had actually turned out to be quite a pleasant experience. He was a neat man in his personal habits, and although he made an unholy mess cooking he did his share of cleaning up afterwards. He'd chopped all that wood for her, tended the fires they'd had, banked them safely at night. In fact, it was very satisfying to have a man like Jerry around the house.

But that didn't mean he was offering her any kind of future. He'd said last night that maybe it was time she took a few chances, that she'd played it safe for too long. He could be right. But it was one thing to come out of her self-protective shell, quite another to walk blindly into what could only be a dead-end relationship. She didn't think she was *that* attracted to him—not yet, at any rate.

Just then Jerry scraped his chair back and rose to his feet. 'Are you about ready to go?' he asked.

'Yes. I just have to get my things.' She got up from the table and started to leave. At the door she turned around. 'What are those errands you mentioned to Patrick?'

'Well, we need groceries, for one thing,' he said. 'The cupboards are bare, and I can't exist forever on toast and crackers.'

Her heart turned over. Clearly he had every intention of staying on with her at the house. But was that wise? Lord knew what Ben would make of that! He must already be suspicious after seeing them together yesterday morning, and she still in her bathrobe!

'Then,' Jerry went on, 'I'll drive you over to Ben's. I want you to try to talk him into letting us take some pictures. Also, when you get the story typed up in final form, he'll need to approve it before I can mail it into the office.'

'All right,' she said. 'Except for one thing.'

'What's that?'

'There's no road to Ben's place, only a narrow path over higher ground through the woods. Even the Land Rover couldn't make it.'

He had come over to her side and was standing quite close to her, smiling down at her. 'Then we'll just have to walk, won't we?'

She gazed up at him, wordless, immobile, as though paralysed by his nearness, and could only nod. Their eyes met, and he reached out to run a hand over her hair.

'Anne,' he said softly. 'Have you thought any more about what we discussed last night? I want you; surely you know that by now?' His hand moved to her face, his long fingers outlining each feature, her forehead, her nose, her lips. 'And I think you want me, too.'

She stepped back from him, alarmed. 'Jerry, at this point I'm not sure what I want.'

The hand dropped from her face and he frowned darkly. 'You're still hung up on Ben Poole, aren't you?'

She turned her head away. What could she say? She was definitely attracted to him and knew she *could* want him if she let herself, but he was moving way too fast for her. She needed more time. And, although it was true that she'd always idealised Ben, since Jerry had come bursting into her life like a rocket from outer space the issue had become distinctly cloudy. How could she explain that to him?

'Well, you'd better make up your mind pretty soon,' he went on coldly. 'I've never had to beg a woman yet, and I'm not about to start now.'

The note of male arrogance in his voice shattered the mood as thoroughly as if he'd dashed cold water in her face. 'Fine,' she bit out sharply. 'No one's asking you to.'

She turned and stalked off down the hall.

The ride into the village was a silent one. Jerry was driving, at Patrick's behest, to get the feel of the Land Rover, and the two men were totally absorbed in an arcane, detailed discussion of the beast's peculiarities and inner workings.

Anne sat in the back, her arms folded in front of her, staring out of the window and brooding over that last conversation. What gave him the right to issue her any ultimatums? She hadn't invited him up here, hadn't thrown herself at him. She'd even done everything in her power to get rid of him! He was so used to having women falling at his feet every time he crooked his little finger at them that...

She gave a start when she realised that Patrick was speaking to her. 'I'm sorry, Patrick. What did you say?'

'I said I expect you'll probably be coming to the get-together at the hotel tomorrow night.'

'Probably not me,' Jerry put in quickly. 'I'll be leaving later today if I can arrange for the seaplane to come and pick me up on such short notice.'

'I thought you were going fishing,' Anne remarked tartly.

'Well, I've changed my mind. I got what I came here for.' He caught her eye in the rear-view mirror.

'Or almost,' he added drily. 'Now it's time to get back to work.'

Anne averted her eyes. He's sulking, she thought with satisfaction. Well, let him! It was nothing to her. Just because he couldn't have what he wanted the exact moment he wanted it was not her problem.

In the village they dropped her off in front of the Sorensons' hotel then drove on to the garage at the end of the street, near the dock, to have the fan belt checked out more thoroughly.

'How long will it take you to do your shopping?' Jerry asked as she got out of the car.

'I have no idea,' she replied brusquely. 'I want to stop in at the hotel to say hello to Carl.' She turned and gave him a saccharine smile. 'But since you have so many errands to do, you should be able to keep busy.'

With a vicious grinding of gears and squeal of tyres, he pulled away from the kerb and left her standing there looking after them. Poor Patrick, she thought, watching the car disappear in a cloud of dust. He must be regretting his offer of the use of it.

She turned and walked slowly towards the hotel. Why had he decided to leave all of a sudden? It was like him, though. He was a man of quick decision, and not all of them right. In her heart, beneath the annoyance at his high-handed, dictatorial manner, she had to admit she'd be sorry to see him go. She'd quite enjoyed his company these past few days, and his interest in her as a woman instead of a story-making machine was flattering. Now all that would be over, and she couldn't quite stifle a pang of regret.

Men! she thought disgustedly as she pushed the door open. Who could understand how their minds worked?

In the kitchen she found Carl, covered in a voluminous white apron and bending over the stove, just taking a fresh batch of scones out of the oven. He looked up when Anne came in and gave her a broad smile of welcome.

'Why, hello there, Anne. Glad to see you were able to make it in at last.'

She went over to the stove. 'Yes, so am I. There's practically nothing left to eat at the house.' She sniffed the fragrant air. 'Those scones smell heavenly, Carl.'

He gave her a sly sideways glance. 'I heard you had some company out there. Fellow from Seattle, isn't it? Came in on Tuesday by seaplane?'

Anne flushed uncomfortably and forced out a laugh. 'My, news travels as fast as ever around here. He's only my boss, Carl. He came up here on business, about a story he wanted me to do, then got stuck at my place because of the floods.'

Carl straightened up. 'Couldn't have been all business. Patrick said he planned to stick around a while, do some fishing.'

'Yes, well, his plans have changed,' she said. 'He's leaving today, as a matter of fact.'

He gave her a long look, then nodded owlishly at her. 'I see. Have a lovers' quarrel, did you?'

'Carl! We're not—I mean, it's nothing like that. He's only my boss. He's leaving early because the story is finished.'

Carl only nodded again, but the dubious look on his face spoke volumes. Anne sighed. Just as she'd feared, Jerry's presence at the house had created a

veritable flood of village gossip. It was just as well he
was leaving.

'I came to see if you've made enough scones to sell,'
she said.

'Sure, Anne. How many do you need?'

'Oh, a dozen or so, if you can spare them.'

He started packing some scones that had already
cooled into a white baker's box. 'You'll be coming to
the party tomorrow night, I hope?' he asked as he
worked.

'Oh, I don't know, Carl.' Now that Jerry was
leaving, it didn't sound like much fun. 'Won't people
think it's a little strange to be socialising so soon after
Dad's death?'

'Of course not. They understand how it was between you two. I think you should come. Everyone
will be there.'

Including Ben? she wondered. Funny how she
hadn't even thought much about Ben since Jerry
showed up.

'Well, I'll think about it.'

Later, as she walked up the street to the grocery
store, she had to wonder why Carl had automatically
assumed Jerry was leaving because they'd quarrelled.
It seemed so very strange to be linked with him that
way publicly. What *was* behind his sudden decision
to leave? Had she actually hurt his feelings by re-
fusing to take his amorous advances seriously?

If so, she thought as she turned into the shop, maybe
he'd really meant what he said about changing.
Everything had happened so fast that she hadn't really
had time to digest it. Now, away from him for the
first time in days, she saw the whole affair in a dif-

ferent light, and it was clear to her that they'd at least
have to have a serious talk before he left.

She dawdled in the grocery store for almost an hour.
It was very crowded with the farmers and other out-
landers who hadn't been able to make it into the village
during the flood, many of them old friends and ac-
quaintances she hadn't seen in years. They all offered
her their condolences on her father's death and seemed
genuinely glad she was back.

She left her purchases at the store so she wouldn't
have to carry the two large bags around with her while
she did the rest of her shopping, and went on down
the street to the general store, which sold virtually
everything else besides groceries on the island. It also
had a Washington State liquor licence. The sherry was
all gone by now and the brandy undrinkable. She
knew Jerry liked Scotch. As she reached for it,
however, she realised that there wasn't much point in
getting liquor for him if he was leaving today, and
she stopped short, her hand still on the bottle. She
didn't want him to go! How could that be? What was
going on?

Finally, with a helpless little shrug, she grasped the
bottle of Scotch more firmly and went over to the
counter to pay for it.

'Anne, Anne.' Someone was calling her name, and
she turned around to see Linda Sorenson over at a
counter, in a darkened corner of the store.

'Hello, Linda,' she said.

'Anne, I need your advice.'

Anne walked over to her. 'What about?'

Linda was holding up a swatch of pale blue silk and
a spool of thread that almost matched it. 'I'm making
a new dress for the party tomorrow night and—

wouldn't you know?—ran out of thread. This seems to be the closest I can get. What do you think?'

Anne took the spool of thread and held it against the material, examining it carefully. 'It's not perfect,' she said at last. 'Let's take it over where the light's better.'

They walked together over to the front of the shop by the window and held it up to the light. 'I think this is probably the best you can do, Linda,' Anne said after a more careful scrutiny. She laughed. 'Take tiny stitches and you'll be all right.'

Just then the door opened and Jerry breezed inside, still grim-faced. He glowered at Anne. 'Are you through with your shopping?' he asked brusquely. Then he did a double-take, his eyes shifted towards Linda, and the frown was gradually transformed into a smile. 'Well, hello,' he said in his most mellow tones. He turned to Anne. 'Well, Anne, aren't you going to introduce me to your friend?'

Anne gave him a sharp look. The expression on his face as he gazed down at the lovely blonde by her side made her feel as though a knife was twisting inside her. Then, just as suddenly, the pain turned into anger. This was one leopard who never had any intention of changing his spots.

'This is Linda Sorenson,' she said through her teeth. 'Her parents run the hotel.' She turned to Linda, who was gazing up at Jerry wide-eyed. 'Linda, meet Jerry Bannister, the editor of the magazine I work for in Seattle.'

The blonde held out a hand. 'How do you do?' she said demurely. 'We've all been wondering about you. You've been staying at Anne's house, haven't you?'

He held on to her hand for so long that Anne was certain in the next moment he'd bend down and kiss it. 'Yes,' she put in hurriedly. 'He came to the house the night of the flood—on business,' she added pointedly. 'And got stuck there until today.'

Jerry dropped Linda's hand at last, but Anne noticed he'd edged a little closer to her in the meantime.

'Oh?' Linda said, batting her big blue eyes up at Jerry in an enquiring look.

'Yes,' he said hastily. 'That's exactly what happened. And now that the road is passable again, I'll be leaving.'

'Oh, not leaving the village, I hope,' Linda cooed. 'You must stay for the party tomorrow night.

'Right,' Jerry said smoothly. 'I intend to. You'll be going, I presume?'

Linda blushed prettily. 'Of course,' she murmured.

They had turned slightly away from Anne, who stood there gaping at them, feeling like an interloper, certainly a fifth wheel. They were completely ignoring her, and she watched, fascinated, at the little by-play that was almost like a mating ritual. Linda was asking Jerry what he thought about the match between the thread and the material, and he was studying them seriously, as though it were the most important question he'd had to consider for years.

'I think it'll do,' he said at last. He gave them back to Linda, his hand lingering on hers in the process. 'You know, that fabric is the exact colour of your eyes.'

'Oh, do you think so?'

Anne had had enough. She didn't care what he thought he was doing, but, whatever it was, she had no intention of witnessing it one second more. She'd already paid for the Scotch, so was stuck with it, but all she wanted now was to get out of there.

'Jerry,' she said. Then, when he didn't answer her, she called more loudly. 'Jerry!'

His head came around at last and he gave her a blank look, as though wondering who in the world she was. 'Yes? What is it?'

'If you've finished your business with the car, I'm ready to leave. I just have to pick up the shopping at the store.'

He gave her an abstracted nod. 'All right. I'll meet you out in front and give you a lift home.' He turned back to Linda. 'I also have to pick up my things. Anne very kindly let me stay at her place, but I've over-stayed my welcome, I'm sure. Do you suppose your parents could give me a room at the hotel?'

Anne brushed past them and stalked off down the street. What a disgusting display! Not two hours after he'd been trying to sweet-talk *her* into an affair, he'd come on to a girl half his age. Well, maybe not half, but *years* younger. And he was the one who had been so worried about her being hung up on an older man!

The Land Rover was parked in front of the grocery store, and by the time she'd stowed her bags in the back seat she had calmed down enough to wonder what in the world had made her fly into such a rage. Granted, it was a flagrant, disgusting display, but what was it to her? He was the kind of man who had to try to make love to every attractive woman who came along, especially if she was blonde, and she'd been a fool to imagine his feelings for her were anything but more of the same.

She sat in the front seat waiting for him for a good five minutes, until finally he came ambling down the street towards her, the luscious Linda by his side. His dark head was bent down towards her, and she was looking up into his face, laughing. The knife twisted again inside Anne at the sight.

I'm jealous, Anne thought with a sudden blinding flash of revelation. Jealous of a man like Jerry! She should be congratulating herself on her narrow escape! And she'd imagined he could change! She'd actually been on the verge of falling in love with the rat! Thank heaven she'd come to her senses in time.

The ride back to her house was a silent one. She glanced over at him from time to time, and the pleased look of smug satisfaction on his face only strengthened her determination to get him out of her mind, out of her heart, out of her life, for good.

'So,' she said, breaking the silence. 'You've decided to stay on after all.'

He shrugged. 'Well, it'd be a shame to miss the party as long as I'm here. It's Thursday, after all— almost the weekend. No point in going back just yet.'

'And I take it you'll be moving to the hotel today?'

He nodded. 'I think so. I've imposed on you long enough.'

'Linda's a beautiful girl, isn't she?' she asked sweetly.

He smiled. 'Yes, she is.'

'Blonde, too.'

'Yes, she is that.'

'A little young for you, don't you think?'

His jaw tightened and he flicked her a quick sideways glance. 'Isn't that rather like the pot calling the kettle black? If you will recall, your May-and-

December romance with Ben Poole has been the subject of more than one heated discussion. It seems to me you were pretty anxious to defend the concept when it was something *you* wanted.'

It was almost as though he was throwing her at Ben. From the beginning he'd simply assumed there was something romantic between them. She was almost beginning to believe it herself. Perhaps Jerry had been wiser on that subject than she'd realised. Dear Ben— so stable, so sensible, so *real*! Let Jerry have his little fling with Linda. It wouldn't last any longer than all the others.

'All right,' she said at last. 'I'll give you that. But what about the story?'

'There's enough for you to finish on your own. It was darned good work, Anne, and will make a fine feature article. I thought I'd use it in the January issue. All we really need now is to get some pictures, and I have every confidence you can talk him into it.'

'Well, all I can do is try.'

They had reached the house by now. Jerry helped her carry in the groceries, and while she was putting them away in the kitchen she could hear him back in her father's bedroom packing his things. When she came to the bottle of Scotch, she hastily took it out of its wrapper, and was just about to stow it away on the top shelf of the cupboard so he wouldn't see it, when she suddenly heard him come in.

She turned around, the incriminating bottle still in her hand, to see him standing in the doorway, his typewriter case in his hand. He came walking slowly towards her.

'You'll probably be needing this,' he said, raising the case. Then he raised his eyes. 'What's that?'

She laughed nervously. 'Oh, since there really wasn't anything here fit to drink, I thought I'd replenish the liquor supply.'

'I see.'

He held her gaze in his for a long moment, frowning slightly, as though wanting to say something but not quite able to get the words out. Then he raised a hand towards her, and she suddenly knew that if she gave him the slightest sign of encouragement they could pick up again where they'd left off. She was even tempted. But just in time she thought about the way he'd fallen all over Linda, and her pride wouldn't let her bend.

She shoved the bottle in the cupboard and closed the door. 'Besides,' she said, turning back to him, 'Ben likes Scotch.' This was a flagrant lie, since Ben didn't drink at all, but she had to think of something. In no circumstances did she want Jerry to know she'd bought it for him.

His lips tightened into a grim smile. 'Of course. We must do everything in our power to please Ben, mustn't we?'

A sharp retort, a reminder of his own feckless behaviour, was on her lips, but she let it die. What was the point? There was no future for her with Jerry. She'd been a fool ever to imagine there might be. It was better this way.

After he had stowed his gear in the Land Rover, said a curt goodbye and driven off, she ran directly to the telephone to call Ben. At the first sound of that deep reassuring voice, all thoughts of Jerry Bannister and his chequered love life fled her mind.

'If you're not too busy, Ben, I'd like to come over to your place after lunch and show you the story.

Remember, you have the right of approval. We won't print one word you object to.'

'It's finished, then?' he asked. 'That was quick work.'

'All except the pictures. How do you feel about my taking some photographs? Or maybe you already have some we could use.'

'I don't know, Anne. Let me think about it.'

'Then it's all right if I come over?'

'Of course. I'm always delighted to see you; you know that. Why don't you come for lunch? I made a big bowl of chilli last night, and you can help me make a dent in it. How does that sound?'

'Wonderful. I've always loved your chilli, Ben.'

'Well, why not come right away, then?'

They ate lunch in the studio. When they were finished, Anne got out the camera and snapped some photographs of his work and the interior of the studio, which was all he'd agreed to. 'Nothing personal,' he'd said. 'Just about the work.'

While she worked, Ben read over the story, and when he'd finished he handed the manuscript back to her. 'This is fine, Anne,' he said. 'Very flattering, in fact. I'll probably even get a few sales out of it.' He laughed. 'Although I'm still not sure how I got talked into it. That Jerry of yours is quite a salesman.'

'He's not "my" Jerry at all, Ben,' she said with a frown. 'And I've been most anxious to explain that whole business to you—you know, why he was there when you came over the other day.'

He held up a hand. 'You don't need to explain anything to me, Anne. I'm just glad you've found someone.'

She shook her head vigorously. 'No! It's not like that! Please believe me, Ben, Jerry is only my boss. Nothing more. I didn't want him to stay. In fact I didn't even know he'd come to the island, but I couldn't very well turn him out when he showed up, with no way back to the hotel.'

'I see. Then you and he are not...?'

'No. Absolutely not.'

'All right. If you say so. I can see you'd rather not talk about it.' Suddenly he stepped back a pace and gave her a long close look, eyeing her carefully, examining her face as though trying to memorise it. 'I'd like to paint you, Anne,' he said at last. 'You have a fresh loveliness that would make a fine portrait—all that wonderful colouring, with your dark hair and fair skin.' He put a hand on her cheek and turned her head slightly. 'A three-quarter pose, I think. How about it? Would you have time to sit for me?'

He was so dear to her, so comforting, a great bear of a man whose very presence made the world seem like a safer place, and so unlike men like Jerry, who had to make everything into a game, to keep women off-balance with their clever talk and one-track minds.

She'd always loved Ben, but, except for that old adolescent crush, had never really thought about him in a romantic way—not until Jerry began harping on the subject. Not only had he been deeply in love with his wife, but he'd always thought of Anne as a little girl, a child. Somehow she'd have to make him see that she was a woman now, a woman who had the power to make him happy again. She swallowed hard and cleared her throat. It was now or never.

'Ben,' she said in a rush, 'have you ever thought of marrying again?'

He gave her a startled look and his brow creased in a frown. 'No. Never. It's never even crossed my mind. Why do you ask?' Then he smiled. 'Anne, you're not still interviewing me, are you? Remember, you promised, nothing personal.'

She waved a hand in the air. 'Of course not. It was only a—a rhetorical question, an old friend's natural curiosity.' Come on, she goaded herself, get on with it. 'No, that's not true.' She took a deep breath. 'Actually, I had a more personal reason for asking.'

'I don't understand.' He was clearly perplexed at her roundabout meandering.

'I—I guess what I really want to know,' she said haltingly, 'is whether you've ever thought of me that way.' She fluttered her hands in a nervous gesture. 'You know, the way a man feels about a woman.'

As the light dawned, his eyes flew open and he actually moved back a step, just as though he'd been struck. He stared at her, open-mouthed, then turned and walked over to his work-table. He stood there with his back to her for several seconds, while she waited, hardly daring to breathe.

Slowly he turned around, his expression grave. 'Anne,' he said in a low voice. 'What can I say?'

'Just tell me the truth, Ben,' she replied shakily. 'That's all I ask. I'm not asking you to make any promises, or even give me any hope. I know how you've grieved for Victoria. And maybe there never will be another woman in your life.' She knew she was saying too much, but now that it was out at last she couldn't stop herself. 'But if you let me, Ben, maybe I can make you forget your pain, or at least diminish it.'

He shook his head slowly from side to side, then came over to stand before her. He put his hands on her shoulders and gazed down into her eyes.

'Anne, I don't know what to say. I've loved you all your life; you know that. To me you've always been the lovely daughter we never had. But it never entered my head——' He broke off, shook his head again and let his hands drop.

'I understand,' she assured him hastily. 'You don't have to say anything more.' She stumbled over the chair by the door where she'd left her jacket, and started struggling into it. 'I'll be going now,' she said. She couldn't look at him. 'Maybe I'll see you again before I leave.'

Her hand was on the door, ready to open it and run, when his voice cut through the stillness like a knife. 'Anne!'

She turned around slowly to see him coming towards her. 'Yes?' she said in a small voice.

He was smiling down at her. 'I didn't say I didn't like the idea, only that such a thing never occurred to me. You'll have to give me some time to digest it.'

She nodded wordlessly.

'I'll tell you what,' he went on. 'Why don't we go to that party together tomorrow night? If it's a nice night we can walk. Otherwise I can probably borrow Patrick's Land Rover or Carl's jeep and drive out to get you. Then we can talk again. How does that sound?'

'Fine,' she said. 'It sounds just fine.'

## CHAPTER SEVEN

ANNE spent the next morning revising her story and typing it up in final form. Tonight she'd leave it at the hotel for Jerry, along with the roll of film she'd snapped. He could have it developed and let the art department decide which shots they wanted to use.

It was another fine day. Although there had been frost on the ground that morning, it had melted by noon. As she worked, her mind kept wandering. She'd find herself gazing out of the window at the pale sunshine, half expecting to see Jerry, or listening for the sound of his footsteps in the house.

But Jerry was gone, she would remind herself sternly, hot on the trail of the first blonde to come along. She'd been a fool to imagine he could change or ever had been seriously interested in her. She couldn't compete with those long-legged beauties of his.

And tonight she'd see Ben. He was the important man in her life now, a man who made her feel safe, cared for, protected. Although he'd obviously been shocked at her suggestion that they might be more than friends, he hadn't rejected the idea outright.

After lunch she made another half-hearted attempt to clear out her father's desk and go through his papers, but after fifteen minutes gave it up as a hopeless cause.

Late that afternoon she went outside to check around the foundations for signs of flood damage from the recent torrential rains. The house was built on high enough ground so that there was no actual danger, but water did tend to collect in the low spots and had been known in the past to seep into the crawl space underneath the house.

When she came to the back yard, the first thing her eye fell on was the huge old cedar stump where Jerry had chopped the wood for her. Behind it, under cover of the lean-to attached to the barn, was a neat stack of logs, with the axe and the heavy gloves he'd worn laid on top.

Although she'd done her best to put all thoughts of him out of her mind, now, at this reminder of him, she found herself wondering how the little affair with Linda had progressed by now. Probably quite a way, considering what she'd seen in the general store at their first meeting. Immediately a vision rose up in her mind of Jerry and the lovely blonde, standing close together, their arms intertwined, kissing . . .

No! she thought. She must not even think such thoughts. It was nothing to her what they did. She turned away hastily from the woodpile and made tracks for the other side of the house. What happened between her and Jerry had been a dream, a fairy-tale. Ben was the reality. He was the kind of man she wanted, and in just a few short hours she would see him again.

She shivered, suddenly cold, and looked up to see that the sky had started to cloud over again. It looked as if there was more rain on the way. Soon a few tentative drops began to fall, and she ran inside the house just as the telephone started to ring.

It was Ben. 'I just called to tell you that I arranged to borrow Patrick's Land Rover tonight. It seems we're in for more rain after all.'

'Yes, I know. I was just outside when it started.'

There was a short silence. Anne waited, wondering if he'd come to any conclusions about their talk.

'Well, I just thought I'd let you know,' he said at last. 'I'll be by around seven o'clock, if that's all right.'

'Fine,' she said. 'I'll be ready.'

After she hung up she stared down at the telephone for some time, frowning. It had been a disappointing conversation, much too brief, and nothing of a personal nature in it. He'd sounded so distant, so formal, so unlike their old easy camaraderie.

At six o'clock she made herself a bowl of soup. There was always so much to eat at the village parties that there was no point in having a real dinner beforehand.

After her bath she went through the clothes she'd brought with her, trying to decide what to wear. The locals tended to dress up for these affairs, but since she hadn't intended to stay long she could find nothing even remotely resembling a party dress. The skirt to her black suit might do. She could wear the white silk blouse with it, and her pearl earrings. But the blouse needed washing and she didn't have time. Ben would be here in half an hour. Why didn't that thought cheer her up?

Dressed in half-slip and bra, she stared glumly into the mirror over her dresser. What a sight! Her shoulders were slumped forward in defeat, her eyes glazed, her brow furrowed. Her hair, still damp from her recent shampoo, hung in limp strands around her pale face, and she had nothing to wear. At this point she didn't even want to go!

But she knew she had to go. There was no way out of it at this late date. It struck her then that if Jerry had stayed on in hot pursuit of Linda he'd most likely be at the party. She couldn't let him see her looking so shabby! With his ego he'd think she was pining away for him!

Then she had a sudden inspiration. She ran into the bedroom her parents had shared, went straight to the huge walk-in wardrobe and flung open the door. On one side were the few things of her father's that were still left hanging. On the other, far in the back, just as she'd hoped, were some old dresses of her mother's.

She pulled out the four closest and laid them on the bed, then stood back, examining them carefully. She'd be ten years out of style, but that wouldn't matter—so were the rest of the women on the island. There were two dresses that might work, and one in particular caught her eye—a lovely sea-green silk with a bluish tinge to it that was just the colour of her eyes, as it had been her mother's.

She slipped into it hastily, fumbling with the back zip, the tiny hook at the top, buckling the wide belt, then stood in front of the mirror to take a look. It was perfect! The fit was a little loose, but if she tightened the belt another notch it would do. Her mother had loved pretty clothes, even though she seldom had had an opportunity to wear them, and had chosen timeless styles. This dress had a wide, rather low neckline with tiny sleeves, tapered down to a narrow waistline, then billowed out in a full skirt. It looked a little dated, but was so flattering that she didn't care.

Tucked way back in the wardrobe she found a pair of high-heeled silver shoes which just fitted her, and thanked her stars that Ben was coming in Patrick's car. She could never have walked the half-mile to the village in them.

She used the blow-drier and curling-tongs on her hair until it fell in soft dark waves around her face, then applied some subdued make-up. Her pearl earrings would have to do for jewellery, but the dress didn't need much decoration anyway. It was lovely enough by itself. She was just putting the finishing touches on her eyes when she heard a car pull up outside and in a few minutes there was a knock on the front door.

Ben! She gave her reflection one more quick look, decided it was at least a vast improvement over the sorry sight it had been half an hour ago, and ran to answer the door. When she reached the hall, she hesitated. Did she look cheap? Ben was such a conservative man. Maybe he'd think she was trying to seduce him.

She reached into the hall cupboard, pulled out her black raincoat and slipped into it hurriedly, knowing full well she was being ridiculous since he'd see her at the dance anyway, but not quite yet ready to let him see her dressed in her party finery. Then she opened the door.

'Hello, Ben. Right on time, I see.'

He stepped inside. 'And so are you. That's nice. I like promptness in a woman.'

Although he had obviously made an effort to dress up, he still looked as though he'd just come from his studio after a hard day's work. He had on the same heavy dark trousers and plaid flannel shirt he usually wore, and his only concessions to the festive occasion were a black knitted tie and a pair of shoes instead of boots.

'Shall we go?' he said.

'Yes. Just let me get my manuscript. I want to give it to Jerry tonight.'

'Oh?' he asked, raising an eyebrow. 'I thought he'd left.'

'He left my house,' she explained. 'But the last I heard he planned to stay on at the hotel for a while. I can leave it with Carl at the desk.'

They didn't have much to say to each other on the short drive into the village. Anne was wrapped up in her own thoughts, on pins and needles wondering what was going through Ben's mind, and Ben, unused to driving, was giving all his attention to it. The rain had stopped for a moment, but the leafless branches glistened in the moonlight from the earlier shower.

When they reached the hotel and he'd parked down the street from it successfully, he finally turned to her just as she started to get out.

'Just a minute, Anne,' he said gravely. 'I think we need to talk.'

She turned to him, hardly daring to breathe. 'All right.'

'I've been thinking over our conversation yesterday,' he went on. He laughed. 'In fact I've thought of nothing else. I must say, Anne, when you drop a bombshell you don't fool around. I was—I still am—stunned by the implications of the things you said, about your feelings, about us.'

'Ben, maybe I was wrong to——'

He held up a hand. 'No, you weren't wrong. You were absolutely right. Anyway, what I wanted to tell you was that, after I got over the initial shock, I must say the idea began to appeal to me more and more.'

'It did?' Anne was stunned. She'd been so prepared for a rejection that it was the last thing she'd expected to hear.

He nodded. 'Although art is basically a solitary oc-cupation, every artist needs a Muse, an inspiration, an emotional support of some kind. Victoria pro-vided that for me beautifully, as you know, and I thought it was gone forever. Now, to my aston-ishment, you've come along.' He put a hand on her arm. 'My only concern is that you're so young, that there's so much difference in our ages.'

'Oh, not that much!' she assured him hastily. Her heart was beating fast. She felt exalted. He wanted her to take Victoria's place in his life! She could hardly believe this was really happening. It was the fulfilment of all her childhood fantasies. She put a hand over his. 'But, Ben, does that mean you care for me?'

'Of course I care for you. I always have. Only now I care in a different way. And if you're truly certain you're not going to regret tying yourself to an older man, to be that inspiration, that support for a de-manding artist, I see no reason why we shouldn't marry right away. You could sell your place and move in with me.'

As he spoke, something strange seemed to be hap-pening to her, a creeping sense of dismay. Marry him? Move into his house? What about her apartment in Seattle, her job? She'd been so sure he'd turn her down that she simply hadn't thought that far ahead. Did she really want to spend the rest of her life playing Muse for his inspiration? During all the years she had adored him he hadn't paid the slightest attention to

her—at least not as a woman. Now, when *he* wanted
it, he was rushing her off her feet.

He was watching her, waiting for her answer. She
looked over at him, wondering how to tell him he was
moving too fast for her, but at the sight of that dear
face, those kind eyes, the security of his big bearlike
presence, she smiled and squeezed his hand.

'Ben, I'm overwhelmed. I never dreamed you—
you'd...' She faltered, unable to go on.

He laughed lightly. 'I think we'd better go inside
now. We can talk about it later.'

As they got out of the car and started walking
towards the entrance of the hotel, faint strains of
music drifted out on the evening air, the sound of
voices, laughter. The party had obviously begun.

Inside, both the lobby and the dining-room were
decorated in a Thanksgiving motif—oranges, browns,
golds, rusts—in honour of the approaching holiday.
Carl's work, Anne knew, as she admired the black
turkey cut-outs, the basket of coloured gourds on the
counter, all very festive.

They were among the last to arrive, and the dining-
room was already crowded. These gatherings were
virtually the sole source of entertainment in the remote
village, so isolated in the autumn and winter months,
and eagerly anticipated by the natives, several of
whom were already dancing with abandon in the
centre of the room to a lively pop tune.

All the tables had been moved against the walls to
clear the centre of the room for the dancing. Three
local amateur musicians were playing loudly and with
gusto on an old upright piano, a violin and a trumpet,
making up with volume and enthusiasm what they
lacked in artistry.

On one of the tables sat an enormous cut-glass bowl filled with a pale pinkish-coloured fruit punch, which Anne knew from past experience was liberally laced with vodka. There were several plates of food set out around it on a wide variety of plates, all supplied by local housewives.

Although there were several faces Anne didn't recognise, she was amazed at how many people were familiar to her from the old days, and soon was caught up in a round of greetings. Patrick was there, looking uncomfortable in a rusty black suit at least a size too small for him, as well as the local grocer and his wife, the owner of the general store, the harbourmaster, the local garage mechanic, and several farmers and their families.

Edith and Carl were there of course, and Linda in her slinky new blue silk dress. As Anne scanned the room she saw no sign of Jerry. Perhaps he'd left after all. She had brought the manuscript and the roll of film in with her, and while Ben chatted with one of the local sheep ranchers she made her way through the crowd to Carl, who was standing by the table ladling out punch.

'Hello, Carl,' she said, raising her voice above the din. 'Quite a party.'

'Hello, Anne,' he shouted. 'Glad you could make it.' The music stopped just then, lowering the decibels considerably, and he stepped back a pace, eyeing her appreciatively. 'My, don't you look nice.'

Patrick came wandering over just then, and stood before her, his mouth hanging open, bug-eyed and staring. 'Anne? I'll be horn-swoggled! For a minute there I thought it was your mother. You're the image of her. She used to wear a dress just like that one.'

Anne laughed. 'Well, as a matter of fact it's her dress. I found it still tucked away in her closet. Apparently Dad never threw any of her things out after she died.'

She turned to Carl. 'I wanted to ask you if Jerry Bannister was still staying with you.' She held up the envelope containing her story. 'If he is, I'd like to leave this for him, but if he's left already I can mail it to him in Seattle.'

'No, he's still here,' Carl replied. He looked past her. 'In fact, here he comes now. You can give it to him yourself.'

She turned around slowly to see Jerry walking towards the table, with Linda, stunning in her sky-blue dress, hanging on his arm and laughing up into his face. Anne's heart turned over at the sight. He was grinning down at the lovely blonde, and looking very handsome in a formal dark suit Anne had never seen before, crisp white shirt and muted tie. He was extremely well turned-out, in fact, with no sign of the rumpled look she was used to.

When he looked up and saw her, the broad smile faded, his eyes narrowed and he stopped dead in his tracks. 'Hello, Anne.'

She handed him the envelope. 'I didn't know if I'd see you again before you left, so I brought along the story to give it to you tonight.'

He took it from her. 'Did you finish it?

'Yes. It's in final form. Ben has seen it and approves.'

'Good. How about the pictures? Did you get any?'

She nodded. 'The roll of film I shot yesterday is inside.'

Jerry turned to Linda, who was still hanging on to his arm, and patted her hand. 'This is just some business I have to get out of the way. I'll be back shortly.' He flicked a glance at Anne. 'You come on along with me. I may need your help.'

She opened her mouth to protest, but he had already turned and was making his way through the crowd. She stared at his retreating back for a moment, hesitating. Although he was treating her exactly as he did in the office—boorish, arrogant and demanding—she was still a little nervous about being alone with him.

Finally, with a sigh of resignation, she hurried after him as fast as she could through the crowd, almost tripping in the unfamiliar high heels. When she caught up with him, she tapped him on the shoulder. He turned his head and raised a heavy dark eyebrow at her.

'Well?' he said curtly. 'What is it?'

'Can you please just wait a minute?'

'Why?'

'I want to tell Ben where I'll be.'

'What for?'

'Well, it's only polite since I came with him.'

He gave her a cold stare, the deep brown eyes narrowed at her, and finally nodded. 'All right. But be quick about it.'

'Yes, sir!' she snapped. By now she was getting a little fed up with his high-handed manner. He'd got what he wanted. Why was he picking on her?

She turned and made her way over to Ben, who was standing in a corner with three of his cronies. She explained the situation to him briefly, but for Jerry's benefit made the short exchange look like a lovers' tryst, placing her hand on Ben's arm and smiling up at him adoringly.

By the time she came back, Jerry was already stalking out into the lobby, and she had to run to catch up with him. When she reached the foot of the stairs that led to the guests' rooms, he was already halfway up them.

She stopped at the bottom and called up to him. 'Jerry.'

He turned around. 'What is it now?'

'Where are we going?'

'To my room.'

She shook her head slowly. 'I don't think so.'

He gave her a disgusted look. 'Oh, for heaven's sake, Anne, what do you think I'm going to do? Rape you?' He came back down a few steps and stood there looking at her, a mocking smile playing about his thin mouth. 'Is it me you don't trust?' he asked softly. 'Or is it yourself?'

'Neither. I just don't see any reason to... I mean, if we go to your room alone, people will misunderstand.'

'You mean Ben will misunderstand.' He smiled blandly. 'We're going to my room because it's the only place around here where we can have a little peace and quiet. I'm sure Ben trusts you. It'll take half an hour, then you can go back to him. Come on, Anne, don't be difficult.' He turned from her and started back up the stairs.

Finally, reluctantly, she began to climb after him. At the landing, he turned right into a narrow hallway. He stopped at a door halfway down, reached in his pocket and pulled out his room key. She stood to one side while he unlocked the door, then followed him inside. After he'd flicked on the overhead light, she made straight for the one chair against the wall, averting her eyes from the bed opposite it. She sat down and crossed her legs decorously, pulling the full skirt over her knees.

Jerry closed the door and turned to lean back against it, a quizzical half-smile on his face. 'So,' he said, 'you came with old Ben tonight.'

She lifted her chin at him. 'That's right.'

'Does that mean you've got him all sewed up nice and tight, the way you wanted?'

She gave him a withering look. 'That's a pretty crude way of putting it, but if you mean do I owe him some explanation about my actions, then yes, it does.' She took a deep breath. 'In fact, tonight Ben asked me to marry him.'

For several moments Jerry stood absolutely still, not uttering a word. Then he asked quietly, 'And are you going to?'

She looked down at her feet. 'I'm not sure,' she said in a halting voice. She gazed up at him again. 'I think so.'

'Well, congratulations,' he bit out through his teeth. 'You worked a lot faster than I gave you credit for.'

She folded her arms in front of her and glared at him. 'You're one to talk! What about Linda?'

'What about Linda?'

'Won't she object to your being alone in your room with another woman?'

'Why should she?' he shot back immediately. 'Linda has no claim on me.'

'No. Of course not. You'd never allow that, would you, Jerry?'

He gazed down at her for a long time, his eyes
guarded, his expression unreadable. 'I might have,'
he said at last in a low voice, 'once. But the lady was
hung up on another guy.'

She was so taken aback by this totally unexpected
statement that she couldn't for the life of her think
of a single thing to say. He turned abruptly from her
and strode over to the side of the bed. It was probably
better to say nothing anyway, she thought. He didn't
mean it, and even if he did she was already half committed to Ben. She folded her hands in her lap and
watched while he sat down on the bed and took her
manuscript out of the envelope.

As he read, she glanced nervously around the room.
It was quite small, but extremely tidy. The bed was
neatly made, his dark blue robe laid carefully at the
foot of it. Beside her chair, on the floor, sat his open
suitcase. A few crisply folded shirts lay on top, and
she quickly looked away.

The door to the adjoining bathroom was open, and
through it wafted faint traces of the masculine scent
she had come to associate with Jerry from his stay at
her house. Suddenly, all the anger drained out of her.
It hadn't *all* been bad. They'd spent some quite
pleasant hours together there. A strange, unexpected
yearning rose up in her at the memory.

Quashing it down quickly, she glanced over at him.
He was totally absorbed in his reading, sitting in a
typical pose, his broad shoulders hunched over, his
feet flat on the floor, his long legs spread apart,
holding her manuscript loosely between his fingers—
long tapering fingers that evoked a more intimate
memory of their time together. She gritted her teeth
and lowered her eyes to her hands, twisting now in

her lap, struggling in vain to blot out her wayward thoughts.

I've got to get out of here, she said to herself grimly, and had half risen to her feet when she heard the bedsprings squeak. She looked up to see him walking towards her.

'This is really good work, Anne,' he said, gazing down at her with a smile of satisfaction. 'Your writing has improved immensely since you've been with the magazine. You have a much surer touch now, and really know how to say what you mean, instead of imitating someone else.'

She beamed up at him, pleased. 'Do you really think so?'

He nodded. 'In fact, I think it would be a good idea to collect some of your best stories and look into getting them published in book form. I have some contacts in the business, and, while I can't promise anything, I think it would be worth a shot.'

She rose slowly to her feet. 'Jerry, I'm overwhelmed. It's been my dream to freelance eventually, but I didn't feel I was ready yet. Do you really think they're good enough?'

He shrugged. 'Well, there's only one way to find out, and that's to try.'

As they stood there, quite close together, smiling into each other's eyes, the atmosphere between them altered subtly. The room began to seem quite warm to her, even in the thin silk dress, yet at the same time a cold shiver ran up and down her spine.

'You look very beautiful tonight, Anne,' he said at last in a low intimate tone. 'In fact, I've never seen you look quite so lovely. That dress suits you. It's the exact colour of your eyes.'

She tried to speak, but her throat was dry and her mouth seemed to be filled with some sticky substance that kept her tongue fastened to the roof of her mouth, her lips glued together.

'I've been doing a lot of thinking since yesterday,' he went on, staring down at the floor. 'We seem to have got off on the wrong foot here.' He gave a diffident shrug and raised his eyes to hers. 'Can't we start over?'

He had moved a step closer to her so that their bodies were just touching now. She searched desperately for the words that would stop him, but she still couldn't speak. She could only stand there, as though mesmerised, watching his dark head bend towards her. The next thing she knew, he had reached out for her and, with a little choking noise deep in her throat, she had fallen into his arms.

His lips were on her forehead, her eyes, her cheeks, then finally on her mouth, pulling at it, as though to draw the very life out of her. As her hands snaked up around his neck and she clung to him tightly, his lips parted and his tongue pushed past her lips, filling her mouth.

Finally, with a low groan, he tore his mouth away from hers and moved it to her jaw, her neck, coming to rest at the base of her throat. She closed her eyes and let her head fall back, totally lost in a thrilling torrent of mindless surrender. At that moment she would have given him anything he asked of her.

One hand was moving across her breasts now, which were heaving and straining against the thin material of her dress, his long fingers skimming over the bare flesh above the low-cut bodice. The hand that still gripped her waist moved downwards, clutching her hips, pulling her tightly up against him so that she could feel his hard arousal pressing urgently on her thigh.

She felt his cheek pressing against hers, the slight scrape of his jaw, his hot breath in her ear. 'Does Ben do that to you when he kisses you?' he murmured.

Her head was spinning around so fast that she couldn't think straight. How could she know what Ben's kisses did to her when she'd never really experienced them? Not like this! The hungry, seeking mouth, the hand on her breast, the naked desire, were totally absent in her relationship with Ben.

He raised his head then and the glittering dark eyes gazed down directly into hers. 'You can't marry him, Anne. I won't let you.'

At his words, the spell was broken, and she suddenly realised what she'd been doing, what she had *allowed* him to do to her. She must have been out of her mind. Shakily, she drew back from him, turned her head away and covered her face with her hands while she struggled for control.

After a few moments, she heaved a deep shuddering sigh and dropped her hands. 'You have nothing to say about it,' she mumbled in a dull voice. Then she looked up at him. 'It's too late anyway. It's all decided.'

He ran a hand over his thick hair in obvious frustration. 'God, and I thought I knew women! How could I have been so wrong?'

'What do you mean?'

'I figured if I stepped aside for a while, let you go on with your campaign with no more interference from me, you'd get it out of your system, come to your senses and——'

'And what? Turn to you?'

He stiffened. 'Why not?'

'And just what do you have to offer me? A good time? A merry-go-round ride? Fun while it lasts and soon forgotten? This is all some kind of game to you, isn't it, Jerry?' Anne said heatedly. 'Well, I can't operate that way, even if you can. Besides, I already told you. It's too late. And, even if I didn't want to marry Ben, I couldn't give myself to a man who didn't care anything about me. I'm just not built that way.'

He shifted his feet uncomfortably and gave her a hangdog look. 'Who said I didn't care about you? I *do* care, Anne.'

She laughed. 'Oh, Jerry, do you think I didn't notice the way you tripped all over yourself the first time you laid eyes on Linda Sorenson? Another blonde, I might add.'

His mouth dropped open. 'Linda Sorenson! She's just a kid!' He gave her a crooked boyish grin. 'That was just habit. I only said I'd help her find a job if she decided to come to Seattle.'

She eyed him balefully. 'If you think Linda is "just a kid", you know a lot less about women than I've given you credit for. She's already packed more experience in her twenty years than I have in my entire life.' She shook her head. 'Go play with Linda, Jerry. She's more your style.'

He moved his face closer to hers and narrowed his eyes at her. 'Can't you get it through that stubborn head of yours?' he gritted through his teeth. 'I don't *want* Linda!'

'But you want someone like her, and, believe me, I'm not it.' She lifted her chin and squared her shoulders. 'Besides, I'm committed to Ben now. He's what I want, what I've always wanted.'

She turned from him and marched over to the door, her head held high. Terrified that if she looked back at him just once she'd never make it, she opened the door and got out of there as fast as she could.

Down in the lobby, Ben was standing at the bottom of the stairs, his hand resting on the banister, gazing up with a troubled expression on his broad craggy face. When he saw her, his eyes lit up and he slowly began to climb the stairs to meet her.

'I was just about to come looking for you,' he said, putting an arm around her shoulders. 'I was beginning to get worried.' He laughed. 'Somehow I don't quite trust that Jerry Bannister of yours.'

She gave him a shaky smile. 'Oh, you don't have to worry about Jerry. All he wanted was to go over the story with me. He liked it very much, by the way.'

'That's good. Now, do you feel brave enough to risk dancing with me?' he asked as they continued on towards the dining-room. 'I warn you, however, I have two left feet.'

In the dining-room, the lights were dimmed and the small orchestra was playing a slow dance tune. As Anne moved into Ben's arms, his body solid and sturdy next to hers, she knew she'd done the right thing.

Just then, across the floor, she caught sight of Jerry, his dark head towering over most of the other men on the dance-floor. He'd obviously followed shortly after she'd left. He was dancing with Linda, their bodies pressed closely together. Her arms were twined around his neck and she was gazing up at him with a secret intimate smile. As they came closer, she could see the familiar glint in his dark eyes that told her exactly what his plans were for the lovely blonde.

It had been a narrow escape, but thank heaven she'd come to her senses in time.

She looked up into Ben's familiar, good, kind face. 'I've decided, Ben,' she said softly. 'I do want to marry you.'

# CHAPTER EIGHT

'ANNE, are you sure?' Ben asked on the way home that night.

Anne looked over at him. He was hunched over the steering-wheel, his big hands gripping it hard, squinting at the road ahead. She was already beginning to regret that she'd blurted it out quite that way. Had she actually said she'd marry him? She should be ecstatic. Instead she was suddenly filled with doubt.

It was all Jerry's fault. His kisses still burned on her mouth, and she brushed the back of her hand over it, as though to wipe out the memory. If he'd been satisfied with Linda and left her alone she wouldn't be in such a muddle. He had nothing to offer her.

'Yes,' she replied firmly at last. 'Positive.'

He gave a deep, low chuckle. 'I never expected anything like this would ever happen to me again. You've made me very happy.'

When they reached her house, she turned to him. 'You'll come in, won't you? We have a lot to talk about, so many plans to make.'

'Not tonight, I'm afraid.' He gave her an indulgent smile. 'We'll have plenty of time for that. I still have to go back to the village and pick up Patrick so he can drive me back to the crossroads. He needs his car early tomorrow morning.'

'Have you ever thought of getting a road paved to your place?' she asked, disappointed. 'It would make it so much more convenient.'

He laughed. 'The village elders have been trying to talk me into doing just that for years.'

'Well, why don't you?'

'Because if there were an easier access to my home, it would utterly destroy my privacy,' he explained patiently, as though to a child. 'I've fought hard for it, and I'm not going to have a steady stream of cars descending on me.' He gave her a troubled look. 'You understand, don't you, Anne?'

'Yes, of course,' she said in a subdued voice. 'In any event, I certainly know how important your work is to you.' What she didn't say was that she wasn't so sure it would be to *her* advantage to have to walk every place she wanted to go after they were married.

'I know you do,' he said. 'And now you're going to be my sweet inspiration, aren't you?' He put an arm around her shoulders and hugged her to him. 'Let's go. I'll walk with you to the door.'

She had left a light burning on the front porch, and when she'd unlocked the door and pushed it open she turned to him. 'Are you sure you won't come in just for a few minutes?'

'No, better not. Patrick will be waiting for me.' He put a hand on her face. 'Why don't you come over tomorrow? I want to get used to having you there while I work. You can spend the whole day, and I'll cook up some more chilli for supper.'

'All right,' she said dubiously. 'If that's what you want.' Then she brightened. 'I'll tell you what, why don't I cook dinner for you tomorrow night? I stocked up on groceries yesterday, even laid in a couple of steaks.'

He pursed his lips, thinking. 'I'd really rather you came to my place. It interrupts the flow of my work to have to leave it, even for a day. It's why I rarely go out.' He smiled down at her. 'Tonight was a big exception, you know. I went to that party just for you. Besides, I want to get started on your portrait. The first of many, I hope.'

He bent down to brush her lips softly with his. 'Goodnight, Anne. See you tomorrow, then?'

She nodded. 'Yes. Of course.'

'Come early. The light is best in the morning.'

With a little salute, he turned and hurried off down the path. She pushed the door open slowly and went inside the dark, cold house.

For the next several days, Anne trudged dutifully over to Ben's house, through sunshine and rain, even a light snowfall on Tuesday, and by the following Thursday she was growing a little resentful of the fact that she had to do all the travelling while Ben sat in his warm, cosy house so absorbed in his painting, hour after hour, that he hardly paid any attention to her.

She hadn't heard anything from or about Jerry, and she assumed he'd either gone back to Seattle, or was off somewhere else with Linda, doing what he did best—making love. Somehow she couldn't bear to think about that, and, no matter how many times she reminded herself that Jerry was nothing to her, thoughts of him kept coming, betraying her every time.

She should have warned Linda about him, she thought that afternoon while she sat for Ben in the studio. All her talk about the blonde's wealth of experience in affairs of the heart had only been smoke, trying to belittle the poor girl. As she pondered this, her mouth became set in a grim line and she squirmed uncomfortably in her chair.

'Don't move around like that,' Ben snapped. 'And try to keep those facial muscles relaxed.'

'Sorry,' she muttered, and tried to do as she was told.

To be perfectly honest, she was getting sick and tired of holding the awkward pose for what seemed like hours, days, years. Her legs, tucked beneath her, ached all up and down from her ankles to her thighs, and her face felt frozen in place. If she twitched or shrugged or sighed or even *breathed* too hard, Ben would lay his brush down and come over to set her in position again.

Was this what her married life was going to be like? They had set the date for Christmas. It was now the middle of November, and Anne saw no point in waiting. His reason for the delay was that since she had insisted on a short honeymoon he wanted to get the portrait finished first. His idea had been to just stay on at his house after the wedding, but she'd finally talked him into a long weekend in Vancouver.

On Friday she decided she just couldn't take any more of it. She called Ben early that morning to tell him she was going to take the day off and walk into the village to do some shopping. It was a clear sunny day, and she wanted to take advantage of it.

'Oh,' was all he said.

'I'm sorry to disappoint you, Ben,' she said, immediately contrite. Her tone had been a little sharper than she'd intended. 'If it's really important to you I can probably come over later this afternoon.'

'No, no, you might as well take the whole day. You've been such a great sport about the sittings. I want you to enjoy yourself.' He laughed. 'I wonder if you haven't changed your mind about getting stuck with a dedicated artist? I can't say I'd blame you. We're a selfish breed, I'm afraid.'

It wasn't that, she thought after they'd said goodbye and hung up. She admired his work, his dedication so much that even the discomfort of the endless posing didn't trouble her unduly. What really worried her was that, except for a few chaste kisses, Ben had made no moves whatsoever towards serious lovemaking. Was it possible that he envisioned their marriage as a celibate one?

In the village, the first person she ran into as she was passing by the hotel on her way to the grocery store was Linda Sorenson. She was just coming out, a heavy blue jacket on against the chill wind blowing up off the straits, and had stopped a moment to tie a scarf around her head.

'Anne,' she called. 'Wait a minute. I've been wanting to talk to you.'

'Hello, Linda.' As Anne waited for her out on the pavement, she glanced behind the girl, half expecting to see Jerry right behind her. But there was no sign of him.

Linda took her by the arm and they started off down the street together. 'I hear you're going to marry Ben Poole,' she said as they walked along. 'What a surprise that was!'

'Oh, really? Why do you say that?'

Linda shrugged. 'Oh, I don't know. He just seems so—so——' She shrugged. 'Well, he is quite a bit older than you. Of course, there's nothing wrong with that,' she added hastily. 'Ben's great. Everybody loves Ben.' She laughed. 'I guess the real reason I was so surprised was that I thought you and Jerry had something going.'

Anne stopped short. 'Whatever gave you that idea?'

'Well, he did stay at your place for a couple of days.'

'That was purely business.' Anne started walking again so briskly that Linda had to run a little to catch up with her.

'Well, I was just positive it had to be more than that,' she said breathlessly.

'I don't see why.'

'Well,' Linda went on, 'you know the night of the party?' Anne nodded. 'I noticed that he never took his eyes off you. I don't know all that much about men, but I do know when one of them is smitten. He showed all the signs.'

Anne had to stop again and stare at the girl. 'Linda,' she said slowly, 'you must be mistaken. In fact, I thought that you and Jerry...' She shrugged. 'You know.'

Linda threw her head back and laughed. 'Oh, don't get me wrong,' she said when she'd sobered. 'I think he's the dishiest man I've ever met, and the most fascinating. But he's way too old for me. He told me that himself.'

'He did?'

Linda nodded. 'He was just being nice to me. I'd asked him about getting a job in Seattle, and he said he'd help me if I ever decided to take the plunge.' She sighed. 'I'd do anything to get out of this hole, and it's nice to have a friend in the city.'

'Then I take it he's gone?' Anne asked.

'Oh, yes. He left the day after the party. Just called the mainland to see if they could send up a seaplane, and off he went, an hour later.'

They had reached the grocery store by now. Anne said a hasty goodbye and turned into it, anxious to get away, to absorb the startling bit of information she'd just heard.

During the next few days, Anne went through all the motions of life, cooking, feeding herself, cleaning, dressing, bathing, but from time to time she would catch herself wandering from room to room, wringing her hands and moaning softly to herself, totally confused, caught in a trap she didn't know how to extricate herself from.

She started making excuses to Ben, and even manufactured a slight cold. She simply couldn't face any more of that awful sitting, and was terrified by now that the very expression on her face would betray her feelings, no matter how hard she tried to hide them. She wasn't even sure herself what those feelings were, except that they disturbed her terribly. The truth was, she was beginning to doubt whether she really wanted to marry him.

Finally, by Monday, she knew she'd have to take some positive action, make a definite decision, or she'd go mad. She'd promised to marry Ben, and that was what she would do. If Jerry really did care anything about her—anything beyond a brief fling, that was—he would have called her by now.

She was also feeling a little guilty about her prolonged idleness. After all, she'd come up here in the first place to get her father's affairs in order, and she hadn't even begun to straighten out his desk.

She marched herself over to it now, sat down, took a deep breath, and opened the top drawer.

By evening she'd managed to plough through most of it. She'd ended up with two enormous piles, which now sat on the floor beside her chair. One consisted of things to be thrown out, the other matters that still needed attention, such as unpaid bills, business correspondence and the few people who still needed to be notified of his death. She'd give those to Mr Pembroke to handle.

By dinnertime she was thoroughly sick of the whole mess. There was only the large bottom drawer left to be cleared out, and she'd save that for tomorrow.

As she got up from the desk and wandered into the kitchen, she suddenly felt very lonely. She hadn't been to Ben's for several days, and she missed the company. She'd picked up a nice leg of lamb at the village yesterday that was far too large for one person. She'd be eating it for days if she didn't share it with someone. It was dark out, but not raining. Maybe she could talk him into walking over.

When she dialled his number the telephone rang and rang, and she was just about to give up when he finally answered it.

'Yes?' he barked gruffly.

'Hello, Ben. It's Anne. I was wondering if you'd care to walk over a little later and have dinner with me. I have a nice lamb roast I'm just about to put in the oven——'

'Sorry, Anne,' he broke in. 'I'm just putting the finishing touches on your portrait, and don't want to stop working.'

'Oh. I see. How is it coming on?'

'Quite well. I think you'll like it. I could use another sitting or two. Maybe you could come over tomorrow?'

'All right,' she said. 'I'll do that.'

'Good. I'll see you then.'

After she'd eaten, had a bath and made a fire, using the technique Jerry had taught her, she still felt rather at a loose end. If she was going to spend the day at Ben's tomorrow, she might as well tackle the last of her father's papers.

The one remaining cluttered drawer consisted mostly of old sheep records, years out of date, and a few personal letters to distant relatives. She didn't even bother to read them. Most of the people were long dead anyway, and she tossed it all on the junk pile to be thrown out.

Then, at the very bottom, she found a long envelope with her name and Seattle address written on the front in her father's familiar hand. It was already sealed and stamped. He'd obviously intended to mail it. Why hadn't he? She reached for it and held it in her hands for a long time, listening to the fire crackling behind her, almost afraid to open it.

Slowly she tore it open. It was dated just a month ago.

Dear Anne,

I have been thinking of writing this letter to you for a long time, but never seemed to get around to it. Today I received some news from the doctor that impels me to do so while there is still time. What I want to say to you is that I was wrong for the way I treated you that last summer you were here. Not a day has gone by that I haven't regretted it. When I lost your mother I was a crazy man. There were times I didn't want to go on living, and you were so much like her that every time I looked at you I was reminded of my loss. I know that's no excuse, but I ask you to forgive me anyway. As it turned out, you were right to leave, and I've been very proud of your success.

It was signed simply, 'Love, Dad.' Short and to the point, just like him. By the time Anne finished reading all her old love for him came flooding back into her heart and head, and the tears were pouring down her cheeks. Her mind was filled with visions of the past, the way he used to be before her mother died, the good man, the devoted husband and caring father he once was.

She folded up the letter and put it back in its envelope, her last gift from her father, a priceless gift. From the bottom of her heart she forgave him, and she was certain that somehow he knew it.

She didn't know how long she sat there, reliving scenes from her childhood, picturing her father in her mind, but when the tears finally stopped and she looked around the room the fire had gone out. She wiped her eyes and blew her nose and looked at her watch. It was almost midnight!

She dabbed at her eyes again, but her handkerchief was so sodden by now that it was useless. She got up and stumbled down the hall to the bathroom to get a tissue. As she fumbled for the box in the dark, she knocked her jar of shampoo off the counter. With a sigh, she got down on her hands and knees, and was groping around on the floor for it, when her hand came upon a small hard object.

She picked it up, got to her feet and turned on the light, holding it out in the palm of her hand to examine it. It was a man's cuff-link, obviously a good piece, a square-cut onyx with a narrow gold band around the edges. She turned it over. Etched in fine script on the back were the initials J.B.

She drew in a sharp breath. It had to belong to Jerry. He must have dropped it there when he was staying with her. Funny he had never mentioned that he'd lost it. But then she'd never seen him wear cuff-links. Probably it had just been stuck away in his shaving kit, and he never even missed it. She had to smile. It was just like him to carry around one useless cuff-link and then lose it.

She suddenly had an overwhelming urge to hear his voice. She hadn't seen him or spoken to him since the party. Surely it wouldn't hurt to call him just to ask how the pictures had turned out. She didn't have his home number, but she could call directory enquiries to get it.

'Oh, why not?' she said out loud to the empty room. Quickly, before she could change her mind, she ran down the hall to the telephone. Then she realised she didn't even know his real first name. Everyone called him Jerry, and that's how he signed all his letters. She snatched up the receiver, called Information and asked for a number for Jerry Bannister in Seattle. She stood there tapping her foot impatiently until the operator came back on the line.

'We have a Jeremy Bannister listed.'

Jeremy! A nice name. 'Yes,' Anne said. 'That's it.'

The operator gave her the number, and Anne dialled it. After eight rings there was still no answer. Of course, she thought, he wouldn't be home. He wasn't the home-loving type. He was probably out with one of his blondes. She was just about to hang up when she heard his voice.

'Hello?' He sounded out of breath.

A little thrill of excitement ran up and down her spine at the sound of his voice. She opened her mouth, but now that he'd actually answered she didn't know what to say.

'Hello?' he said again.

Slowly, carefully, she replaced the receiver in its cradle.

From then on, to her utter dismay, Anne began to see reminders of Jerry everywhere in the house—the way he'd screwed the top on the peanut butter jar so that it didn't quite fit, how he'd thrown silverware into the drawer instead of stacking it neatly.

She even looked for traces of him in her father's bedroom. She knew it wasn't possible, that he'd left nothing behind, but it seemed to her that she could still feel him in the silent room, smell his distinctive scent. He'd filled the house with his presence, and now it seemed empty without him.

She began to think she was losing her mind. What did Linda know about his feelings? She had no idea what kind of man he was. Well, what kind of man was he? Did she really know him herself? She knew his reputation, but what did that have to do with the way he'd treated her?

She reminded herself over and over again that, even though his desire for her had been unmistakable, he was a man who didn't make commitments or promises to women. Still, that desire, all by itself, was highly flattering, something she'd never expected from him.

And he'd been so complimentary about her work, the story about Ben she'd written, encouraging her to pursue her writing as though *her* career, *her* future, was important to him. Unlike Ben, who only seemed to view her as an inspiration for his painting.

The one thing she was certain of was that before she could marry Ben she had to work the residue of whatever it was she felt for Jerry out of her system.

She awoke the next morning to the patter of rain against the window. She rose up and stretched widely, refreshed from the soundest sleep she had had in years, still warmed by her father's lovely letter. She jumped out of bed and ran to the window, pulling aside the curtains.

It wasn't raining hard, but she wasn't thrilled at the idea of going out in it. She regretted her promise to Ben of another sitting today for the portrait. She just didn't want to go. Two weeks ago she would have jumped at the chance. What had happened in the meantime to change that?

When she finally did set out for Ben's a few hours later, it was still raining, and by the time she got there she was thoroughly soaked. As she stood on the porch shaking out her raincoat, the door opened and Ben appeared.

'Anne,' he said, beaming. 'I'm so glad to see you.' He held the door open. 'Come on inside where it's warm. Sorry you had to walk through the rain like that.'

'Oh, that's all right,' she said, moving past him into the warm house. 'I finally finished going through my father's papers yesterday, so there wasn't much to do at home anyway.'

'Let's go into the studio. I've got a fire going and you can dry out in front of it.'

When they got to the studio he made straight for the easel, which was covered with a white cloth. 'I want to show you what I've done so far on the portrait.'

She sat down by the fire and watched expectantly as he slowly uncovered the canvas. Ben was one of those artists who would never allow anyone to look at his work until it was finished, and she was anxious to see how it had turned out. He'd been so undemonstrative since their engagement that she had no grasp of how he really felt about her, and she was hoping that the portrait would give her a clue. Had he pictured her as a young girl? A *femme fatale*? His future wife?

'There,' he said. 'What do you think?'

She rose up and stared at the painting, open-mouthed. It was the last thing she had expected to see. There, on the easel, was almost an exact duplicate of the portraits he had done of Victoria after her death. She didn't know whether to be flattered or dismayed. She walked slowly towards the easel. The colours he'd used, the pose, even the expression on her face, were all the same.

But I'm not Victoria, something inside her screamed. I'm me! He was watching her, obviously waiting for her to say something.

'Of course,' he said when she remained speechless, 'it's not really finished yet. That's why I need a few more sittings. I'm not quite satisfied with the angle of the jaw.' He put an arm around her shoulder, laughing. 'But we'll have years ahead of us to perfect it, won't we?'

Like a flash of lightning, it broke in on her fuddled mind that from the very beginning Ben's only really concern had been her usefulness to him. She didn't blame him. He'd said it himself. Without a pretty broad streak of ego, artists couldn't create at all. He'd needed her to be his Muse, he'd said, his inspiration. Was that all their life together was going to be?

Automatically she found herself comparing him with Jerry, the man she'd always thought of as so arrogant and self-centred, and particularly about their last conversation, the encouragement he'd given her about her writing, offering to help her get published, even though it might mean losing her services on the magazine. He'd been thinking of *her* work, *her* future. Was that so selfish and arrogant? And she remembered the little ripple of excitement she'd felt last night just at the sound of his voice.

She looked over at Ben, who was still waiting for some reaction from her about the portrait, *his* work, *his* project, and for the first time he appeared to her as he really was. Nice, safe, solid Ben! But good old Ben cared about as much for her as he did for that portrait sitting on the easel. Less, in fact. To him she was only an adjunct to his deep commitment to his art, and that just wasn't good enough.

As she gazed at him now through such different eyes, it seemed to her that he had aged overnight. He looked like an old man, and somehow she connected this change in him with the letter from her father. It dawned on her then that Jerry had been right all along with his warning that she was only looking for a father figure.

She shook herself free of Ben's encircling arm and stepped back a pace from him. He was looking at her with a puzzled expression on his face.

'Anne,' he said, alarmed. 'What is it?'

She gazed at him, wide-eyed. 'I can't marry you, Ben,' she said shakily.

'What?'

'I can't marry you!' This time her voice was much firmer. She shook her head. 'It just wouldn't work. Don't you see? You don't really want a wife. And even if you did, you certainly don't want me. I'm sorry. It's all my fault. It's just that I was so crazy about you when I was a young girl, and after my mother died my father was so awful to me——' She broke off.

'Anne, Anne,' he said. 'You're just upset. I think your father's death has hit you harder than you realised. Here, sit down. I'll make you a cup of tea.'

'No!' she cried. 'I don't want any tea.' She turned from him and started walking away hurriedly. At the door, she turned around. 'I'm sorry, Ben. I hope I haven't hurt you. And I'm sorry to disappoint you about being your inspiration.' She smiled. 'But you'll have to admit you did your best work when you had to do without one anyway.'

He simply stared at her in disbelief for some time. Then he said quietly, 'It's Jerry Bannister, isn't it?'

'No. Of course not.'

He smiled sadly. 'Anne, I'm one of your oldest friends. I know it's not in you to lie to me, but I think you might be lying to yourself. I've seen you together.' He laughed. 'I'm an artist, remember? I've trained myself to pick up on those little nuances of character, emotion, relationships.'

'You're wrong, Ben.'

She stepped back a pace from him, raised her chin and stuck her hands in her pockets. Immediately her fingers curled around a small hard object—Jerry's cuff-link! Why had she put it there? She couldn't even remember doing so!

She was so stunned by this discovery that when she realised Ben was still talking to her she had to make an effort to clear her buzzing head and pay attention to him.

'That first morning I came to your house,' he was saying, 'and saw him there, my immediate impression was that you were lovers.'

'We weren't,' she said in a small voice.

He nodded. 'That's what you said, and I believed you. And when you told me about your feelings for me, I put it out of my mind. He'd left by then anyway. In fact, I thought he'd left the island altogether.' He paused. 'Then I saw you together at the party, and I knew.'

She coloured deeply at the memory of what had gone on in Jerry's room that night. 'But if you remember,' she said, 'it was that very night that I said I'd marry you.'

'Anne, do you think I don't recognise a lovers' quarrel when I see one?'

'Then why did you ask me to marry you?' she cried.

He shrugged. 'Because I wanted you.'

Suddenly she was filled with a certain knowledge of what she had to do. Compared to Ben, Jerry was like quicksilver, with his flashing dark eyes, his wicked grin, his quick decisiveness. He might be feckless and wayward, she certainly had no illusions about any possible future with him, and she knew quite well he wasn't in love with her. But he did care about her as a person. At least she knew where she stood with Jerry, and if he still wanted her, on whatever terms, she'd go to him.

Still clutching the cuff-link tightly in her hand, she gave Ben one stricken look, then turned and started running towards the front door. She heard him coming after her, and when she reached the door she turned around.

'Anne,' he said. 'Where will you go?'

'Back to Seattle where I belong,' she said distinctly. She opened the door and darted outside into the rain.

She ran all the way home, stumbling over the stones and fallen branches that littered the narrow dirt path, as if her life depended on it. She knew now what she wanted, what she'd probably always wanted, ever since the night Jerry had first shown up at her house. She also knew she was taking a terrible risk. He had promised her nothing. He might not even still want her.

When she reached her house, she burst into the front door and ran straight to the telephone, not even stopping to take off her wet raincoat. She just stood there dripping in the hall while she dialled.

'Hello, Mr Pembroke? This is Anne Cameron.'

'Yes, Anne,' came the lawyer's voice. 'What can I do for you?'

'I've finished going through my father's papers and plan to leave today. I'll stop by your office, if I may, and drop off the things that you need to deal with. Then you can put the house on the market. I've decided to sell.'

'Well, all right, Anne, if you're sure. I have a court appearance this afternoon, but if I'm not here you can leave everything with my secretary.'

After they hung up, she dialled Patrick's number, praying he was home. After a few rings, his gruff voice came on the line.

'Patrick, this is Anne. Could you take me across to Roche Harbor today?'

'Well, yes, I guess so. It's raining, but there's not much wind. The channel should be calm enough to make it in good time. When do you want to leave?'

'As soon as you can get here to pick me up.'

'Half an hour, then?'

That was calling it close, but if she hurried she could make it, and she *had* to get across while the weather held. 'Fine,' she said. 'I'll be ready.'

# CHAPTER NINE

IT SEEMED strange to Anne to be walking down Seneca Street again towards her old office building on the corner, yet it was the same bustling city, the same shops, the same buildings, even the same faces.

She'd arrived home late the night before, exhausted from the long dismal trip from the island, and had fallen into bed as soon as she could get her clothes off. She'd intended to take the next day off to unpack and get her bearings and to consider what her next move should be.

That morning, however, she'd awakened at dawn fired with an almost manic sense of urgency. She had to see Jerry again right away, had to find out how he felt about her and what, if anything, the future held in store for them.

As she rode up in the lift to the magazine's offices on the fifth floor, the determination she'd felt earlier began to waver, and when she stepped inside she was seized with a sudden attack of stage fright. She stopped just inside the door and glanced around the large room. It was only nine o'clock and already humming with activity. Telephones were ringing, typewriters were clacking, voices were raised in the usual panic.

She took a deep breath and made straight for Jerry's glass-enclosed office at the far end, waving and smiling vaguely at several of her co-workers on the way. From

their casual offhand greetings, she might have been
gone two hours instead of two weeks.

Jerry wasn't in his office, but the moment she
stepped inside she felt a strong sense of his presence.
It was all so familiar, the raincoat he never bothered
to wear even in Seattle's drizzly climate still hanging
on the hook behind the door, the silver cup he'd won
a few years ago for excellence in journalism from a
prominent literary society, every available surface in
the room as cluttered as ever.

While she waited for him, she glanced idly down
at the mess on his desk. It was as bad as her father's!
There were files, manuscripts, art layouts, photographs, even private correspondence, all scattered
about in an unimaginable litter. Yet she knew from
personal experience that he could put his hands on
the exact item he needed in a second.

Then her eye was caught by a familiar sheaf of
paper off to one side, just about to fall off the desk,
which she instantly recognised as the manuscript of
her story on Ben Poole. She leaned over to take a
closer look. Scrawled across the title page in Jerry's
distinctive slashing handwriting were the words. 'No
emendations. Print as is.' She glowed with pleasure.
What a tribute! It was unheard of for him to approve
a story as written, so rigid were his standards.

Clipped to the title page was a stack of photographs, which reminded her that there was a partial
roll of exposed film still left in the camera that she
hadn't finished shooting. As she flipped through the
developed pictures, however, she could see that what
they already had would be enough.

'Anne!' she heard someone call to her, and she looked up to see Tim Farragut, the art director, coming through the open door.

'Hello, Tim,' she said. 'I see the place is still as busy and disorganised as ever.'

He shrugged comically and made a face. 'What did you expect? That we'd fall apart without you?' He laughed. 'Although I'll have to admit, I missed your smiling face. Did you get all your business taken care of?'

'Yes, at last.'

'Well, it's great to have you back.'

'It's good to be back. I thought I'd better check in with our glorious leader. It's a couple of days past the time off he gave me, and he'll probably scream bloody murder. That is, if he doesn't fire me. Any idea where he is?'

'Well, you're safe enough for a while. The invincible Jerry Bannister has succumbed to a bug. Claimed he picked it up in some ''God-forsaken wilderness'', to use his terminology, but he never did clue us in as to exactly where.'

'You mean he's sick?' Anne could hardly believe her ears. Jerry hadn't been out sick for a day for as long as she'd known him.

Tim nodded. 'He came slamming in here a week or so ago looking like death warmed over and even grouchier than usual, if you can conceive of such a thing. Finally last Friday someone got up the nerve to tell him he'd better see a doctor, and that's the last we've seen of him since then.'

'Well, I don't see much point in sticking around here, then,' she said. 'I still have unpacking to do at home.' She slung her bag over her shoulder and smiled at Tim. 'I might as well play truant while I can get away with it.'

She started to follow Tim out of the door, but not before she had taken a quick closer look at one of the bills lying on top of Jerry's desk. It was addressed to him at his home.

He lived in the Madrona District, on a street near the western shore of Lake Washington. It was an older part of town that contained some of Seattle's most palatial mansions, as well as smaller cottages in between, its streets narrow and winding, conforming to the contours of the lake.

When she reached his street, she drove by slowly. His house was in the middle of the block, set well back from the road, with a small but impressive garden in front. It was quite bare now in November, but it looked well cared for and, from the curving row of rose-bushes that lined the drive, must be lovely in the summer.

She parked across the street, and sat there for a good five minutes debating whether this was such a good idea after all. Perhaps it was premature, or taking too much for granted, to barge in on him like this at his home just on the basis of a few kisses, a few intimate encounters.

Then inspiration hit. She'd put her camera in the glove compartment of the car when she'd picked it up at Roche Harbor yesterday. In it was the half-roll of undeveloped film. She got out the camera, wound the roll to the end, and removed it. It was wasting film, but what did that matter? It would give her an excuse for dropping in on him this way.

Before she could lose her nerve, she got out of the car and marched across the street, then hurried up the path, and rang the front doorbell. She could hear it chiming inside, but there was no other sign of life. After several seconds, she rang it again.

Still nothing. She was just about to give up when she heard someone shouting from inside the house, actually more of a hoarse bark than a shout. 'The door's open, damn it! Come on in!'

She turned the handle and poked her head inside a small entry hall. Beyond it, standing near a doorway at the far end, stood Jerry. And what a sight he was to behold! He was wearing his dark blue bathrobe, which was rumpled and wrinkled as though he'd been sleeping in it for days, and a pair of scuffed slippers.

'Anne,' he croaked, and started walking slowly towards her. 'What are you doing here?'

'I heard you were sick,' she said hastily. She held up the roll of film. 'But thought I'd better drop this off anyway. I forgot to give it to you before.'

He stopped short a few yards away from her, and they stood there for a while just staring wordlessly at each other. He had several days' growth of beard on his face, his eyes were red-rimmed and bleary, his dark hair tousled every which way, and he had never looked so dear to her, so vulnerable.

He was eyeing her more carefully now, as though he'd just realised she was actually here, in his house. Finally he said, 'So, Anne, what brings you back to town? I thought you'd be safely married by now to good old Ben and that's the last we'd see of you.'

'Well, as a matter of fact,' she began, hoping she was doing the right thing, 'that's all off.'

His dark eyes lit up. He gave her a pleased smile and at the same time they each took a step nearer. Then, suddenly, his head jerked back, he sucked in a deep breath, closed his eyes and sneezed loudly into the handkerchief in his hand.

'Better not come any closer,' he said when it was over and he had mopped his nose. 'I think I'm still contagious.'

'Shouldn't you be in bed?' she asked.

He waved a hand in the air. 'How can I stay in bed? I've got too much work to do. I've been stuck here in this damned house for almost a week now.'

He reminded her of a small boy, irritable because he couldn't go out and play, and she had to smile. 'I was just in the office, and they seem to be surviving without you.'

'I don't want to talk about the office,' he said firmly. 'The only thing that interests me is what made you decide not to marry Ben Poole.'

He was so patently pleased at the news, even in spite of his wretched condition, that she knew everything was going to be all right, that she'd done the right thing by coming to him this way.

'Well, as it turned out, and much as I hate to admit it, you were right all along. You see, I found this letter from my father when I was going through——'

Just then the front door opened. Startled, Anne turned to see a tall blonde woman walk inside, her arms filled with grocery bags. She gave Anne a hesitant look, then smiled at Jerry and started walking towards him.

'What are you doing out of bed?' she asked sternly. 'I leave you for ten minutes and the minute my back

is turned you disobey orders. Go on, now, like a good
boy. I got you some nice chicken soup for your lunch.'

Of course, Anne thought. Wouldn't you know he'd
have another blonde on the string the minute he got
back to Seattle? Sick or well, Jerry Bannister still
functioned in the usual way. This one was new to her,
but she had all the old familiar attributes. To her
horror, she felt tears stinging behind her eyes, and her
one thought was to get out of there before she made
an utter fool of herself.

'Well, I'd better be running along,' she said brightly.
'Hope you'll be feeling better soon.'

She turned around and half ran to the door. She
had just grasped the handle and turned it when she
heard him calling to her.

'Wait, Anne. Don't go.'

She turned her head to give him one last look. He
was holding out a hand to her, his eyes pleading. No!
she said to herself, steeling herself against it. I will
not be taken in by that look again! She yanked the
door open and stepped outside, slamming it behind
her.

She drove around for a couple of hours after that,
fighting back tears, torn between disgust at herself
for being such a fool as to think there was a chance
for her with Jerry, and absolute fury at him for
somehow managing to come up with yet another
blonde when practically on his deathbed. If it hadn't
been so tragic, it would be funny.

She stopped at a fast-food drive-in around two
o'clock and choked down half a tasteless cheese-
burger and a cup of coffee. By then she had calmed
down enough to realise she wasn't making sense. What
right did she have to be angry at Jerry? He was a free

agent. He had made her no promises. What did she expect? After all, the last he'd heard of her, she was going to marry another man.

To Jerry, what had happened between them had only been a game. He couldn't help that; it was the way he was made. Might as well condemn the leopard for having spots as blame him for not being able to change.

What a muddle she had made of her life! For one fleeting moment she was even tempted to make a dash for it back to the island and tell Ben she'd marry him after all, but that didn't last long. Not only would it be unfair to him, but she was so sick of making bad decisions that she was almost afraid to do anything.

The real problem was that seeing Jerry today in his weakened condition, pouting over his illness, tousled, rumpled, sneezing, unshaven, had made one thing clear to her that she'd only dimly suspected up until then. She was in love with him!

The question was, how in the world could she manage now to work with him again, see him every day, be near to him, watch his parade of blondes?

It was almost dark by the time she got home, the overcast skies creating a late November dusk. She'd stopped on the way to stock up on food for her bare cupboards and then just wandered around the mall looking in shop windows, trying to collect her scattered thoughts and make up her mind what to do.

When she stepped inside her apartment, her arms laden with groceries, the telephone was ringing. She ran into the kitchen, set the bags down on the counter and snatched up the receiver.

'Hello?'

'It's about time you got home,' came the hoarse voice. 'Where the hell have you been? I've been calling all afternoon—first the office, then your place. I'm a sick man. Don't you have any consideration?'

In spite of her broken heart she had to smile. Above all else, she warned herself, sinking down on the stool in front of the counter, be calm and reasonable.

'Sorry, Jerry. I had some errands to run.'

'Well, what I want to know is why you ran off the way you did.' Then there was a pause as he sneezed. '*Drat* this blasted cold!'

'Shouldn't you be in bed?' she asked mildly.

'I *am* in bed!' he croaked. 'Why did you go, Anne? Haven't you ever heard of succouring the sick? I thought the least you could do was soothe my fevered brow or read to me or feed me some soup.'

'It seems to me you had that pretty well in hand,' she remarked tartly. She hadn't meant it to come out that way, sounding so jealous, but it was too late to unsay it now.

'You mean Sylvia? She's only my doctor's receptionist. She very kindly offered to drop off a prescription for me and do a little shopping. *She* felt sorry for me, even if you didn't.'

'Well, then, you didn't need me, did you?'

'What's wrong? Afraid of catching my bug?'

'Something like that,' she replied drily.

'Well, the doctor tells me I'm no longer contagious, so how about coming back over tonight?'

'I don't think so.'

'But I'm all alone here,' he moaned.

'I think you'll live. Besides, I'm busy. I just got back late last night.'

'Tomorrow, then? You ran out of here so fast this morning that you didn't finish telling me what happened to your great romance.'

She'd had about all she could take. 'Do you really think that's any of your business?' she snapped.

'Yes, I do!' he snapped right back. 'Now, will you come tomorrow or not?'

She sighed. 'I'll see, Jerry. I've been gone for a long time and——'

'I know,' he broke in. 'Exactly three days over the two weeks I gave you.'

'And have a lot to catch up with,' she continued, ignoring the interruption.

There was a long pause. 'Anne,' he said softly.

'Yes?' she said guardedly when he didn't go on.

'I need to see you, Anne. We've got to talk. Please come tomorrow.'

'I'll see. I have to go now, Jerry. Goodbye.'

She quickly hung up the telephone. In one more second she would have started blubbering. '*Damn* the man!' she muttered under her breath. What was it that made him even more endearing in his helpless, fractious condition than he had been in his full confidence and strength? What fools women made of themselves over men! She'd been in love with two men in her life, both of them hopeless.

She got up and started putting groceries away. Of course she wouldn't go see him tomorrow. That was out of the question. It would be fatal.

The next morning once again she sat in her car across the street from Jerry's house, gazing glumly over at it, wondering if she'd trip over another blonde if she

did decide to go in. It wasn't too late to turn back.
She hadn't made any promises.

Then what was she doing here? She'd planned to
go straight into the office, but her car, as though it
had a mind of its own, had driven straight here. She'd
spent a sleepless night, tossing and turning, debating
endlessly whether to come at all, and now, suddenly,
she realised, deep inside her, that she'd come simply
because she couldn't live without him, that she wanted
him on any terms she could get him.

With a sigh, she opened her door, got out of the
car, and walked slowly across the street.

This time he answered the bell when she rang. 'Glad
you could make it,' he said, holding the door open
for her. 'Come on in.'

He was looking much better today, still pale and
drawn from his illness, but far more presentable. He
was clean-shaven, his hair washed and combed, and
dressed in a pair of dark trousers, white shirt and rust-
coloured pullover.

'Take your coat off and go on into the living-room
and sit down. I just made a pot of coffee, and won't
be a minute.'

'I thought I was supposed to succour the sick,' she
said, removing her raincoat and hanging it on the coat-
stand. 'Why don't you sit down and I'll get the
coffee?'

He bowed and made a sweeping gesture with his
hand. 'Be my guest. The kitchen is just down the hall.'

What surprised Anne most about the house was its
cosiness and order. Somehow she had pictured Jerry's
home as a swinging bachelor pad, with red flock
wallpaper, thick pile carpets, gaudy mirrors all over

the place, and, like his office, an untidy mess in general. It was nothing like that.

The kitchen was papered in a cheerful yellow floral pattern, the counter-tops a deeper gold tile, and there were spotless starched white curtains at the corner windows. When she reached up into the cupboard for mugs, the plain white dishes were neatly stacked with orderly precision. On a tray laid out on the built-in stove sat a gaily patterned milk-jug, sugar bowl and mugs, napkins and spoons.

She put the glass cafetière of coffee on the tray and carried it into the living-room, where Jerry was down on his haunches lighting a fire in the white-panelled Adam fireplace. She set the tray down on the coffee-table in front of the couch and watched him, the memory of the fires he'd built while he was with her on the island filling her mind. She was lost by now, and she knew it.

'There,' he said, rising to his feet and heading for the couch. 'That should do it.'

There was still a slight nasal twang to his voice, the last remnants of his flu, but he seemed much better today than he had yesterday. He sat down beside her, poured out the coffee, and they both sat sipping in silence for a moment or two.

'Now,' he said, setting his mug down. 'Tell me what happened with Ben.'

'Oh, Jerry,' she said with a sigh. 'Must I? It was a mistake, and I'm just grateful I caught it in time. I don't want to go into all the gory details.'

'Well, I hate to say it, but I told you so, didn't I? Wasn't I right?'

'Yes, Jerry, you were right.'

'All right, then. You don't have to talk about it if
you don't want to, but I am curious about one thing.
What made you finally come to your senses? Something pretty important must have happened to make
you change your mind.'

She hesitated. Of course something important had
happened. She'd realised she was in love with him.
But she couldn't tell him that. 'Well, it was several
things, I guess. For one thing, Ben is so wrapped up
in his work that he wants a ministering angel to give
him inspiration more than he wants a wife. And for
another, I found a letter my father wrote me before
he died that changed everything.'

He was leaning forward now, his elbows resting on
his knees, a look of deep intensity on his face. 'And
what did the letter say?'

'It was by way of apology, actually, explaining why
he shut me out of his life the summer my mother died.
It doesn't really matter. The important thing is that
it made me realise I was really looking for a father in
Ben.' She lifted her shoulders. 'It was as though when
my real father gave himself back to me through his
letter I didn't need a substitute any longer.'

'I told you that, too, didn't I?'

She turned on him, suddenly angered by the smug
satisfaction written all over his face. 'If you're so all-
fired smart, Jerry, why is it you haven't got your own
act together by now?'

He reared back. 'What do you mean by that crack?'
he snapped.

She made a sweeping gesture with her hand. 'Well,
for one thing, why does a man who surrounds himself
with a decidedly homely cosy atmosphere persist in

avoiding family life? Why haven't you ever been able
to settle down with one of your blondes?'

He coloured deeply. 'You're crazy. You don't know
what you're talking about. Besides, you have no right
to judge my way of life.'

'Oh, no! Of course not!' She glared at him. 'It's
all right for you to go poking your nose into *my*
business, dissect all *my* personality problems. What
makes your foibles so sacrosanct?'

Their eyes were locked together now in angry confrontation, neither yielding an inch. Finally, he started
to laugh. He reached out a hand and tousled her hair.

'You're so cute when you're mad,' he said with a
chuckle.

Then the smile faded and a familiar gleam appeared in his dark eyes. Anne sat mesmerised by that
steady gaze, the tart reply dying on her lips. How
could you fight a man like this? In one word, one
look, he'd swept away all her defences, and she felt
herself melting inwardly, waiting.

'In fact,' he said smoothly, his voice pitched low,
'you're looking especially enticing today.' His eyes
dropped lower briefly, then flicked back up to her face.
'That red sweater suits you. You have just the
colouring—and the body—for it.'

Her cheeks grew warm. She'd worn the red sweater
on purpose that morning, knowing it flattered her
dark hair and pale complexion, as well as her figure.
She felt his weight shift on the couch beside her so
that they were just touching now, and the sudden
warmth of his body next to hers was like a burst of
flame.

He reached out slowly and clasped the back of her
neck with one hand, then placed the other flat against

her cheek. His thumb began to rub gently over her lips in a familiar caress. She was drowning, and she knew it, and she couldn't utter a word.

'We could have some wonderful times together, Anne,' he murmured softly. 'I could take you places you've never been before if you let me.'

All she could do was nod wordlessly. She knew quite well what he meant. In those few short sentences, he was making himself absolutely clear. He was asking her to have an affair with him. She tried to think, but in her heart she knew the time for thinking was long past. It was why she'd come here today, and far too late to turn back. She wanted him on any terms she could get him.

'Yes,' was all she could say, and closed her eyes.

His arms came around her then, holding her tightly up against him. His lips were on her hair, her forehead, her cheek, and his hands were moving over her body. She shivered as they snaked their way under the red sweater, across her bare back, and finally came to rest on her breast.

As the seeking hands worked their magic on her, all thought fled from her mind. She gave herself up to him and the sheer joy of the moment completely, ready to give him whatever he asked of her, wanting it, wanting him.

Then, suddenly, he stiffened. His body grew rigid, his hands stilled and he slowly drew away from her. She opened her eyes to see that he was half turned away, staring into the flickering fire and scowling darkly. In a moment he looked at her again and gave her a brief rueful smile.

'*Damn* this cold!'

He rose abruptly to his feet, crossed over to the fire and stood looking down into it for several long seconds. Anne sat there stunned at his abrupt withdrawal, watching him and waiting for him to explain, to say something. Anything! Of course he'd been sick. Maybe that was the answer. But he wasn't *that* sick if he could get bathed and dressed, make coffee, and at least start to make love to her.

'Jerry,' she said at last, 'what's wrong?'

He waved a hand in the air. 'Oh, it's just this blasted bug.' He still wouldn't look at her.

She didn't believe him. It had to be more than that to make him disappear so completely. Did he need a little prompting? She'd turned him down so many times, maybe he was afraid she'd back out again. Maybe *he* needed some reassurance from her.

'Jerry,' she said slowly, 'I've thought a lot about what happened at the island.'

He leaned down to stir up the fire with the poker, then turned his head to give her an inscrutable look. 'A lot of things happened there,' he said smoothly, 'and not all of them pleasant.'

'No. I know that.' She laughed nervously. 'I don't think I was in full possession of my faculties at the time. But I just wanted you to know that I have thought about it, about the things you said, a lot.'

There was another long silence while he gazed back into the fire. Why wasn't he helping her out? Why was he making this so difficult for her? Did he want her to grovel, to beg? Finally, he stood up and looked down at her, his face bland and composed.

'I do remember encouraging you to try and get a book put together. Have you thought any more about it?'

If he'd struck her she couldn't have been more shocked. 'Well,' she faltered, 'that's one thing.'

'I still think it's a good idea, and I'm perfectly willing to give you all the help I can.' He laughed. 'Of course, I don't want to lose you on the magazine. But then you have a pretty iron-clad contract. I see no reason why we can't work it out.'

She had to get out of there, and now, right away, before she did something she'd regret for the rest of her life. What she felt like doing was throwing something, slapping the cold smile off his face, screaming at him. Instead she drained the last of her cold coffee, just for something to do while she collected herself.

Then she rose to her feet. 'Thank you,' she said. 'That's very generous of you. I'll appreciate any help you can give me. Now, I think I'd better go. I don't want to tire you.' She started walking towards the hall, where she'd left her coat.

He jumped to his feet and held a hand out to her. 'Anne,' he said in a low voice.

She turned slowly around. 'Yes?'

He was frowning down at the floor, his face working, and when he raised his eyes to hers there was a haunted look in them. 'Nothing,' he said curtly at last. 'I'll see you to the door.'

'Better not,' she said, hurrying away from him. 'I wouldn't want you to have a relapse.'

# CHAPTER TEN

ANNE drove blindly along the city streets, her cheeks burning, her hands shaking. What a humiliating experience! You'd think she would have learned what he was like, she agonised, from all the years she'd known him! 'Never again,' she swore through her teeth. She'd take a vow of celibacy before she'd ever offer herself to a man again.

Why had he led her on that way only to back off the minute she responded? Was it simple revenge for the way she'd rejected him in the past? But that didn't sound like Jerry. She couldn't even really be angry with him. It wasn't his fault if he'd decided he didn't want her. Why should he be satisfied with second best? She'd turned *him* down after all when he'd wanted her.

It was still only mid-morning when she left, and she headed down town. She knew now what she had to do and was anxious to get the next step over with before she lost her nerve.

At the office, she went straight to the personnel director, a kindly, middle-aged woman who stared at Anne aghast when she informed her that she was leaving the magazine.

'But it's such short notice, Anne,' she protested. 'I don't have anyone to replace you. And you do have a contract with us.'

'Listen, Roberta, you don't need a replacement for me,' Anne replied firmly. 'I only do feature articles, and I can just as well do them on my own. I don't want to be tied to a job any more, but that doesn't mean I can't still do whatever my contract requires.'

'Well, can't you at least wait until Jerry gets back?'

Anne rose from her chair. 'No. I can't do that.'

Roberta gave her a long look of appraisal. 'All right,' she said quietly at last. She stood up and held out her hand. 'Good luck, Anne. We'll miss you around here.'

'Thanks, Roberta. Thanks for everything. I'll let you know where you can reach me as soon as I know myself.'

The older woman's eyebrows shot up. 'Are you leaving town?'

'I might. I haven't decided yet. But I'll be in touch.'

There, she thought, on the way home, it's done. I should have done it ages ago. That's one thing I have to thank Jerry for. If it hadn't been for his encouragement I wouldn't have had the nerve to take such a drastic step.

The first thing she did when she got home was call Mr Pembroke in Friday Harbor.

'Mr Pembroke,' she said when he came on the line, 'this is Anne Cameron. I want you to take the house off the market. I've decided to keep it myself.'

'Well, that is a surprise, Anne. I was just going to call you today to tell you I received an offer on it. Are you sure you don't want to sell?'

'Yes. Positive. I'll be coming back in a few days and will stop by your office to pick up the keys.'

Suddenly there were a million things that needed doing. A permanent move was far more complicated than a two-week trip. She'd set down strong roots in

Seattle. Actually, she was grateful for the distraction. It kept her from thinking about Jerry.

By the following night, she'd packed most of her dishes and other household articles in boxes provided by the removal company, but still had her clothes and personal belongings to get ready. She'd arranged to stop the paper, have the utilities turned off, change her address and inform her landlord she was leaving on Monday, the day the movers were coming for her furniture.

The apartment was already beginning to look bare, unlived-in, with the pictures off the walls, chair cushions and other objects missing. She was trying to eat up as much of the food in the house as possible so she wouldn't have to shop again, and was in the kitchen finishing up a grilled cheese sandwich and a glass of milk when the doorbell rang.

She opened it to see Jerry standing on the other side, his hands on his hips, his face like thunder. 'What's this about quitting your job?' he barked.

She had stepped back from the door the moment she saw him, and now he pushed it open, came inside, and shut it behind him with a loud bang. 'Answer me! Why did you quit your job behind my back?'

'I—I just thought it was time, that's all. You were the one who said I should strike out on my own. Now that I own a house and have a little money, I just decided to take your advice.'

He glanced around the room at the boxes stacked against the wall. 'You're going away,' he said.

'Yes.'

'When?'

'The movers are coming on Monday.'

'Back to the island, I suppose.'

'That's right.'

He glared darkly at her for several seconds. 'It's Ben,' he said at last in a low growl. 'You're going back to him.'

'No, of course not. I told you. That's all over. Ben has nothing to do with my decision.'

'But I do,' he said. She turned away from him, but his arm shot out and he twisted her around to face him. 'What is it, Anne? Why are you really leaving? Have I done anything to upset you?'

'No. Of course not. It's something I should have done a long time ago. It has nothing to do with you.'

He gave her a long look. 'You're lying,' he said at last.

She pulled herself free and started walking away from him. 'I have an awful lot to do, Jerry, and not much time to do it in, but I could give you a quick drink if you like. How are you feeling, by the way? All over the flu, I see.'

'Anne!' His voice cut into the room like a gunshot. 'Anne,' he said in a softer tone, moving to her side. 'Look at me.'

If she did, she knew she'd be lost. She kept her head turned away, her hands clenched into fists at her side, every muscle rigid. Why had he come storming over here like this? She could see that he might be annoyed at losing her from the magazine, but surely Roberta must have explained to him that she still planned to write for him if he wanted her to? Only at a safe distance.

His hands came down on her shoulders and she heard his low voice behind her. 'Anne, you can't go like this. We have unfinished business between us. I—

I——' He faltered, and his hands tightened on her. 'I don't want you to go. I need you here.'

She turned around. 'As I told Roberta, I'll be available for feature articles if you want them. It's not as though you needed me to be right there, under your thumb in the office.'

He shook his head. 'I didn't mean that. I meant *I* need you. Me. Personally.'

'What do you mean?'

He dropped his hands from her shoulders. 'I did a very stupid thing the other day when you came to the house. In fact, I've handled this whole thing between us badly right from the start. But that was probably the dumbest episode of the bunch. The fact is, when you were actually there and seemed, well, interested in me at last, I simply panicked. I was terrified. It was the last thing I'd expected.'

He started pacing around the room, his hands stuck in the pockets of his dark trousers, scowling darkly. Anne didn't know what to say. There was nothing *to* say, not yet. Finally, he came to stand before her again.

'You've got to understand, Anne. Until you showed up, for all I knew you were dead set on marrying Ben, perhaps already had. Then, when you came back, my first thought was that now there was some hope for me. Anyway, to make a long story short, my plan, if you can call it that, was the same as it had always been—to talk you into an affair with me.'

'I knew that,' she said calmly. 'I was even ready for it when I came back the next day. But you virtually sent me away. At the very least, you showed a decided lack of interest.'

'Yes, well, that was the really dumb part,' he said glumly. 'When you started talking about the time we

were together on the island, I knew you were ready
to give in.' He threw his hands up helplessly. 'But
somehow, seeing you there, so brave, so self-giving,
I just couldn't do it. You just aren't that kind of girl.'

Anne's mind was racing. All she could think of was
that he didn't want her to leave. He was obviously
trying to tell her something, but she couldn't quite see
what it was.

'I see,' she said at last. 'But don't you think I'm
the best judge of that?'

He shrugged. 'Perhaps. In any event, that's what
my conclusion was—that a brief affair was no go.' He
sucked in a lungful of air. 'However, the alternative
was not only terrifying, it was something so entirely
new to my way of thinking that I didn't even recognise it until I found out today that you'd quit your
job. Then I knew. I can't let you go.'

She still couldn't quite grasp what he was driving
at. Only one thing was clear to her. He had come back
to her. He still wanted her. And she still wanted him,
on any terms she could get him. A great feeling of
hope settled on her, calming her.

She smiled at him. 'You're not really making much
sense, Jerry, but I think you're saying...' She faltered, not quite sure of herself.

'What I'm trying to say is that I want you, Anne,
on any terms I can get you.'

At his words, so exactly echoing her own, she had
to laugh. At the same moment, they both moved the
step closer that separated them, reaching out blindly,
and the next thing she knew she was in his arms, half
laughing, half crying into his shoulder, the tweed
jacket rough under her cheek.

He held her tightly, as though afraid she'd disappear if he let go, to the length of his body. She raised her arms up around his neck, clinging to him with all her might, while he stroked her hair and murmured her name, gentling her. He pressed his face against hers, his mouth at her ear.

'I want you, Anne,' he murmured. 'I want you so badly.'

She felt as though she was floating mindlessly, giving herself up entirely to the present moment. His hand was moving up and down her bare arm in a soothing, hypnotic rhythm, and her arms tightened around his neck.

'Oh, Jerry, I want you, too,' she whispered happily.

He raised his head to gaze down at her, his dark eyes gleaming. 'Are you sure?' he said in a low voice.

She nodded. 'Absolutely.'

He gave her a quirky smile. 'What happened to my girl who was so hell-bent on safety at any price? Have I created a monster?'

She smiled. 'I don't know. Try me.'

He slowly lowered his head. She closed her eyes, waiting, and when his lips touched hers a deep sense of joy filled her whole being. His mouth was soft, brushing lightly over hers in a slow, sensuous motion at first. Then, suddenly, as though both bursting into flame at once, they clutched blindly at each other, clinging together in a frantic embrace.

Then, wordlessly, in complete tacit understanding, they moved slowly down the hall to the bedroom. When they reached the side of the bed, Anne turned into his arms and raised her face to his. Their lips met again, and as they sank down on the edge of the bed Jerry's mouth opened over hers in sudden urgency.

Under the force of his kiss, she lowered her head back on the pillows. He leaned over her, his hot tongue probing and insistent, demanding entrance. With no thought except for him, she surrendered to him totally, as though this was what she was born to do. As his tongue explored her mouth, his hands moved over her body possessively from her shoulders, over her breasts, then down to her thighs and back up under her skirt, as though wanting to memorise every inch of her.

He tore his mouth away then and pressed his cheek against hers, so that she could feel his hot, rasping breath in her ear. He was lying half on top of her now, their thudding hearts beating in unison.

'God, what you do to me, Anne,' he breathed harshly. He raised his head, his dark eyes boring into hers. 'There hasn't been a day that I haven't wanted you.'

With their eyes still locked together, he brushed one hand lightly over her breasts, then slipped it underneath her thin blouse to rest on her bare midriff. His touch on her skin sent a shaft of liquid fire coursing through her bloodstream. She moaned faintly and closed her eyes as his hand moved slowly upwards, then she sighed deeply when it closed around her breast.

'Sit up,' he whispered, guiding her to an upright position so that she sat facing him.

He tugged upwards on the loose blouse, and she raised her arms so that he could slip it over her head. When she was free of it and he had dropped it behind him at the foot of the bed, he held her arms in place with one hand, while with the other he trailed his long fingers down her upraised arm and bent his head to lay his lips on her bare shoulder.

Then he pulled back from her, releasing her arms, and swiftly removed his jacket before unbuttoning his shirt. 'Touch me,' he said.

Eagerly, she reached out both hands to run them lightly, tantalisingly, over the lithe, sinewy muscles of his strong arms and broad chest. As her fingers trailed lower, fluttering on his flat stomach, he sucked in a deep breath, and she could feel the muscles quivering under her touch. He reached behind her then to unclasp her bra and slip it off.

'You're as beautiful as I thought you would be,' he said in a hushed voice full of wonder.

He placed his large hand over one bare breast, then the other, moving back and forth slowly, first kneading, then barely touching, until she threw her head back, groaning at the sheer ecstasy of the sensations he was arousing in her.

He bent his head then and opened his lips over one taut, thrusting peak, drawing on it, pulling it inside the warm, moist interior of his mouth, his tongue flicking over it, while his hands slid lower beneath the waistband of her skirt.

She was filled with a wild elation, a mindless joy, and could barely suppress a glad cry as she clutched at the dark head at her breast, her fingers raking through the crisp dark hair. His greedy mouth shifted to her other breast, his hands slipped down lower, and she arched her body upwards to feel the full force of his own arousal.

With a low harsh sound deep in his throat, he left her again to pull off the black trousers. When he came back to her, he undid the fastening of her skirt and slid it down over her hips, his fingers lingering along the way on her stomach, her thighs, her legs. He covered her body with his, his breath coming in great racking gasps now, and she put her arms around his neck.

He raised his head, hovering over her for a moment, staring down at her, clasping her face in his hands.

'God, how I want you, Anne,' he ground out.

With a low moan, she pulled his head down to kiss him, and then, at last, they became one, joined together in the deepest expression of love.

The next morning, Anne awakened beside a sleeping man for the first time in her life. As consciousness slowly returned, and she felt the warmth of his body next to her, she raised up and looked over at him.

He was turned towards her, his dark head half buried under the pillow, his broad bony shoulders bare, the covers tumbled loosely around his waist. Her first thought was, What have I done? The second, I'm so glad I did it. He'd been wonderful, warm, tender, considerate of her inexperience, leading her gently but surely to the higher realms of love.

Well, not love exactly, she amended. Although he had whispered endearments to her at the height of his passion, there had been no talk of love, no mention of the future. But she'd known what she was getting into. She'd done it with her eyes open, and she wasn't sorry. Watching him sleep, though, she couldn't help thinking how wonderful it would be to have him with her always.

Just then the body beside her shifted, the head came out from under the pillow, and he turned slowly on to his back, one long arm thrust over his forehead.

He turned slowly, blinked a few times, then smiled sleepily and immediately reached out a hand to her.

'Good morning,' he said. 'And how are we feeling today?'

She nestled cosily against him in the curve of his arm. 'We're feeling terrific,' she replied happily.

'Good.' He raised himself up and braced his hands on either side of her head, gazing down at her. 'It *was* terrific, wasn't it?'

She gave him a stern look. 'I suppose you're already fishing for compliments.'

He laughed. 'No, not really. My compliments are all for you at this point.' He flopped his head back on the pillow and lay staring up at the ceiling for some time. 'Now, here's what I think we should do,' he said at last in a matter-of-fact tone. 'First thing, of course, we'll have to get a licence. I think there's still a three-day waiting period in Washington state. We may need blood tests, I'm not sure, and two witnesses . . .'

Anne had risen bolt upright and was staring down at him, so stunned that she was totally unmindful of the fact that the covers had slipped down to her waist. 'What did you say?' she demanded.

'Mm,' he said, reaching out to cup one bare breast. 'You're delicious in the morning.'

He began making slow circles around the hardening peak. In another minute she'd be lost again. Quickly, she clapped her hand over his, stilling it, then thrust it away and pulled the covers up around her shoulders.

'Would you please repeat that last statement?' she said.

'Gladly. I said you were delicious in the——'

'Not that, you sadist!' she cried. She waved a hand in the air, and the covers slipped again. His hand shot out immediately, and she grabbed it, holding it still. She covered herself once more, quite securely this time. 'I mean all that about blood tests and witnesses and waiting periods.'

'Well, I don't know why you're so surprised. You want me to make an honest woman of you, don't you? An old-fashioned girl like you wouldn't be happy with anything less than a lifetime commitment.'

That wasn't quite what she wanted to hear, and her disappointment must have shown on her face, because his expression grew suddenly serious. He sat up and looked into her eyes. There was a crooked, teasing smile on his lips, but those dark brown depths were dead serious.

'Besides that,' he said in a low voice, 'I'll have to admit that I love you madly and can't live without you.' He shrugged diffidently. 'It's why I sent you away the other day. I knew then that an affair wouldn't work, but, as I said earlier, the alternative was too terrifying even to consider.' He looked away, as though embarrassed at revealing so much of his deeper feelings.

'What made you change your mind?' she prompted.

He smiled at her. 'I already told you—I discovered I was in love with you. I didn't want to lose you.' He stretched widely, yawning. 'Besides, it's about time I settled down. How do you feel about family life? I had in mind at least two little Bannisters, and there's no reason why you couldn't work at home if the idea appeals to you. We could even spend part of the year at the island.'

Anne was speechless, literally struck dumb with joy. She was going to have it all! The work she wanted to do, marriage to Jerry, children, a real home. She gazed at him with glistening eyes.

'Well?' he said at last, shifting uncomfortably on the bed. 'Say something.'

'I love you,' she choked out. 'How's that?'

'That's perfect,' he said, patently relieved. 'Now,' he said with a grin, reaching out for her, 'let's get rid of that blanket, shall we?'

# Next Month's Romances

Each month you can choose from a wide variety of romance with Mills & Boon. Below are the new titles to look out for next month, why not ask either Mills & Boon Reader Service or your Newsagent to reserve you a copy of the titles you want to buy — just tick the titles you would like and either post to Reader Service or take it to any Newsagent and ask them to order your books.

| *Please save me the following titles:* | Please tick | √ |
|---|---|---|
| AN OUTRAGEOUS PROPOSAL | Miranda Lee | |
| RICH AS SIN | Anne Mather | |
| ELUSIVE OBSESSION | Carole Mortimer | |
| AN OLD-FASHIONED GIRL | Betty Neels | |
| DIAMOND HEART | Susanne McCarthy | |
| DANCE WITH ME | Sophie Weston | |
| BY LOVE ALONE | Kathryn Ross | |
| ELEGANT BARBARIAN | Catherine Spencer | |
| FOOTPRINTS IN THE SAND | Anne Weale | |
| FAR HORIZONS | Yvonne Whittal | |
| HOSTILE INHERITANCE | Rosalie Ash | |
| THE WATERS OF EDEN | Joanna Neil | |
| FATEFUL DESIRE | Carol Gregor | |
| HIS COUSIN'S KEEPER | Miriam Macgregor | |
| SOMETHING WORTH FIGHTING FOR | Kristy McCallum | |
| LOVE'S UNEXPECTED TURN | Barbara McMahon | |

If you would like to order these books in addition to your regular subscription from Mills & Boon Reader Service please send £1.70 per title to: Mills & Boon Reader Service, P.O. Box 236, Croydon, Surrey, CR9 3RU, quote your Subscriber No:.........................................
(If applicable) and complete the name and address details below. Alternatively, these books are available from many local Newsagents including W.H.Smith, J.Menzies, Martins and other paperback stockists from 12th February 1993.

Name:..............................................................................................

Address:..........................................................................................

..................................................Post Code:..........................

**To Retailer: If you would like to stock M&B books please contact your regular book/magazine wholesaler for details.**

You may be mailed with offers from other reputable companies as a result of this application.
If you would rather not take advantage of these opportunities please tick box ☐

Mills & Boon have commissioned four of your favourite authors to write four tender romances.

**Guaranteed love and excitement for St. Valentine's Day**

| A BRILLIANT DISGUISE | - | Rosalie Ash |
| FLOATING ON AIR | - | Angela Devine |
| THE PROPOSAL | - | Betty Neels |
| VIOLETS ARE BLUE | - | Jennifer Taylor |

Available from January 1993                          PRICE £3.99

# 4 FREE

## Romances and 2 FREE gifts just for you!

*You can enjoy all the heartwarming emotion of true love for FREE!*
*Discover the heartbreak and the happiness, the emotion and the tenderness of the modern relationships in Mills & Boon Romances.*

*We'll send you 4 captivating Romances as a special offer from Mills & Boon Reader Service, along with the chance to have 6 Romances delivered to your door each month.*

**Claim your FREE books and gifts overleaf...**

# An irresistible offer from Mills & Boon

Here's a personal invitation from Mills & Boon Reader Service, to become a regular reader of Romances. To welcome you, we'd like you to have 4 books, a CUDDLY TEDDY and a special MYSTERY GIFT absolutely FREE.

Then you could look forward each month to receiving 6 brand new Romances, delivered to your door, postage and packing free! Plus our free Newsletter featuring author news, competitions, special offers and much more.

This invitation comes with no strings attached. You may cancel or suspend your subscription at any time, and still keep your free books and gifts.

It's so easy. Send no money now. Simply fill in the coupon below and post it to -
**Reader Service, FREEPOST,
PO Box 236, Croydon, Surrey CR9 9EL.**

---

## Free Books Coupon

**Yes!** Please rush me 4 free Romances and 2 free gifts! Please also reserve me a Reader Service subscription. If I decide to subscribe I can look forward to receiving 6 brand new Romances each month for just £10.20, postage and packing free. If I choose not to subscribe I shall write to you within 10 days - I can keep the books and gifts whatever I decide. I may cancel or suspend my subscription at any time. I am over 18 years of age.

Ms/Mrs/Miss/Mr _____ EP31R

Address _____

_____

Postcode _____ Signature _____

Offer expires 31st May 1993. The right is reserved to refuse an application and change the terms of this offer. Readers overseas and in Eire please send for details. Southern Africa write to Book Services International Ltd, P.O. Box 42654, Craighall, Transvaal 2024. You may be mailed with offers from other reputable companies as a result of this application.

If you would prefer not to share in this opportunity, please tick box ☐